A Director's G

Health and Wellbeing in the Workplace

MANAGING HEALTH, SAFETY AND WELLBEING AT WORK TO BOOST BUSINESS PERFORMANCE

Editorial Director: Tom Nash
Managing Editor: Lesley Shutte
Consultant Editor: Marc Beishon
Project Consultant: Alan Bayley
Production Manager: Lisa Robertson
Design: Halo Design
Commercial Director: Ed Hicks
Managing Director: Andrew Main Wilson
Chairman: George Cox

Published for the Institute of Directors, ABI, DTI and
HSE, with support from IOSH and NHS Plus,
by Director Publications Ltd
116 Pall Mall London SW1Y 5ED
020 7766 8910
www.iod.com

© Copyright October 2002
Director Publications Ltd
A CIP record for this book is available from the British Library
ISBN 1 901580 87 3
Printed and bound in Great Britain
Price £9.95

Contents

THE Chartered Director

Be recognised as a professional director

CHARTERED DIRECTOR

The IoD's Chartered Director initiative ensures directors' continued professional education and development.

CRITERIA

Admission to the profession of Chartered Director is open to all IoD members and Fellows with the requisite qualifications who are able to demonstrate the knowledge and experience required to become a member of the profession and who undertake to observe the IoD's Code of Professional Conduct.

BENEFITS

There are clear personal benefits to becoming a Chartered Director. They are recognised as directors:

- *who have achieved standards of professional knowledge and experience;*
- *who have made a serious commitment to their profession;*
- *who have undertaken to act with probity and honesty.*

The letters *C.Dir* that Chartered Directors may append to their names are an easily recognisable badge of professionalism.

As a condition of continued registration, "chartered" members must commit to Continuing Professional Development (CPD) – at least 30 hours a year keeping themselves abreast of both practical and theoretical developments in direction.

To find out more about becoming a Chartered Director, telephone 020 7451 3210, or visit the IoD's web site at www.iod.com

The IoD is ideally suited to help Chartered Directors achieve their Continuing Professional Development (CPD) requirement.

Look out for this symbol which is displayed on IoD products and publications that can assist directors in achieving their CPD requirement.

Fitter employees equal fitter companies

**George Cox, Director General,
Institute of Directors**

In recent years there has been a sea change in thinking about the health and wellbeing of employees. The last two decades have witnessed a significant – and continuing – rise in concerns about issues such as disability employment, stress and work-life balance. And, government health and safety guidelines now explicitly state that employers are responsible for employees' physical and mental wellbeing.

Whilst all employers must be aware of the regulatory obligations, there are other compelling business reasons for addressing the issue. Apart from the increased risk of litigation, evidence is now emerging that healthier staff contribute more to corporate success. There are likely to be improvements in productivity and creativity, and far fewer problems with absenteeism arising from causes such as badly designed workstations or inflexible childcare arrangements.

The headline figures about issues such as stress, absenteeism and substance abuse only give broad pointers to possible concerns. The following guide offers employers practical advice on how to identify which health and wellbeing issues are specific to their workplace and outlines measures to help address them.

Plus

Bringing
Good Health
To Your Business

www.nhsplus.nhs.uk
Freephone: 0800 092 0062
nhsplus@doh.gsi.gov.uk

NHS Plus offers a full range of occupational
health services including:

- Workplace risk assessment
- Pre-employment screening
- Health surveillance
- Immunisations
- Medical advice on sickness absence or retirements
- Stress counselling
- Training in manual handling and first aid
- Insurance medicals
- Lifestyle screening
- Drug and alcohol screening

Keeping a healthy competitiveness

**Patricia Hewitt, Secretary of
State for Trade and Industry**

Many factors combine to make a truly great company. But, the most important asset of any organisation, whatever its size, is its people. For this reason, health, safety and wellbeing at work are essential factors for any company that is striving to lead its field.

Currently, many businesses fail to recognise the potential competitive advantages for their organisations of taking a pro-active and innovative approach to the care of their staff. There is growing evidence that work-life balance polices, in particular, can help lower absenteeism, reduce staff turnover, improve recruitment and widen the labour pool – all of which are tangible business benefits for companies looking for an edge in competitive and challenging markets.

Promoting and maintaining health, safety and wellbeing at work is not a fad – it makes sound business sense. Stress-related sick leave costs UK industry £370m a year. This is a cost that both business, and the country, cannot afford and we all need to look at new ways in which efficiency and productivity can be enhanced through working smarter and safer.

There is still work to be done to get more companies to seek and implement change. There are no off-the-shelf solutions to work-life balance and wellbeing issues. Every organisation is different and therefore employers, including government, need to look at policies which are appropriate to the needs of the customers and the employees. I believe that employers that instigate change now will be able to reap long-term benefits for productivity, their people and their community.

IOSH, representing around 26,000 members, is the guardian of generalist health and safety standards in the UK.

IOSH is an independent, not-for-profit, non-governmental organisation committed to improving workplace health and safety. We provide analysis and advice to national and international decision-makers on key areas ranging from risk assessment and control, through the changing contexts of employment and work, to health and safety management systems. IOSH is an authoritative source of health and safety advice, guidance and training.

• consultants
Our free client/consultant matching service identifies health and safety specialists with the right skills and experience for a specific project or role.

• advice
www.safestartup.org offers essential, free health and safety information for business start-ups.

• information
Free guidance, technical infosheets and a toolkit for SMEs are at www.iosh.co.uk/technical.

• training
Over 100,000 people every year are trained on IOSH's internationally recognised, high quality, flexible courses. Our 1,000-strong trainer network delivers courses in-house, as scheduled public programmes or via distance learning – including a range of CBT options.
– health and safety training
– risk management training
– environmental training
– health and safety Passport

www.iosh.co.uk
enquiries@iosh.co.uk
t +44 (0)116 257 3100
f +44 (0)116 257 3101

IOSH... for a safer world of work

Chapter 1

Creating a healthier, happier workplace

Marc Beishon, business and health writer, assesses how well UK businesses are doing in managing health and wellbeing in the workplace

EXECUTIVE SUMMARY

- In 2001, employees across all sectors took an average 7.1 days sick leave, costing business £476 per individual.

- According to the HSE, around five million UK workers describe their job as 'very stressful'.

- Increasingly, larger organisations are using the services of employee assistance programme (EAP) providers.

- Many health and safety issues cross over into statutory responsibility.

Over the last decade there has been a sea change in the way that we think about work-related health issues. Traditional attitudes towards health and safety – with the emphasis more on safety – have been replaced by the recognition that people interact with modern workplaces in complex, multi-factorial ways that affect both health and wellbeing.

There are several landmark trends and actions that have had a direct bearing on workplace health policies:

- *The recognition that stress and work-related upper limb disorders (WRULDs) are important workplace health factors;*

- *Legislation and guidelines that place heavier responsibility on companies for employee's mental health and wellbeing;*

- *The Working Time regulations and the impact of long working hours;*

■ *Greater demand for flexible working policies;*

■ *An increasing body of work about the impact of cultural change on organisations in the light of constant rounds of mergers and downsizing.*

The government has implemented two ten-year health and safety strategies, both of which are the responsibility of the Health and Safety Executive. The first, *Revitalising Health and Safety* – launched in 2000 – has pinpointed key targets for improvement. These are to reduce: the proportion of working days lost from work accidents and ill health by 30 per cent; the incidence rate of fatal and major injury accidents by 10 per cent; and, the incidence rate of cases of work-related ill health by 20 per cent. The strategy is aiming to achieve half the improvement under each target by 2004.

The second, *Securing Health Together*, is a complementary long-term strategy, that is focused on occupational health issues through work programmes that include compliance with good health and safety practice, continuous improvement through knowledge, networking and partnerships, promoting skills required for implementing occupational health, and support and advice.

THE COST OF ABSENTEEISM

With the range of health-related issues widening constantly – from back pain, bullying, sick-building syndrome, corporate manslaughter, alcohol, smoking and drug policies, to HIV/AIDS – it's clear that employers need to take action. Perhaps the most persuasive motive is financial. For example, there is no shortage of evidence, in the national press and elsewhere, highlighting the cost to business of absenteeism.

According to the CBI's 2002 Absence and Labour Turnover survey, absence from work levels have reached their lowest. At the same time, the cost of absence has risen, as employers have started to take more factors into account in their calculations, such as loss of productivity. Overall, the CBI survey found that employees across all sectors were absent for an average 7.1 days in 2001, at a cost of £476 per individual.

CASE STUDY: GOLDMAN SACHS

The rewards of investment banking may be high, but so too are the potential risks to health and happiness

But when Goldman Sachs, one of the world's leading investment banks, launched its wellness programme in 1997 this was no low-calorie move to preserve its position in the fast lane.

The Wellness Exchange, which is at the heart of Goldmans' workplace health and wellbeing programme, came out of a concerted effort by senior executives to develop a people strategy that complemented and supported its business strategy. The resulting investment has translated into a unique and integrated programme, but the underlying principle is simple: if your people are your greatest asset then they must be properly cared for.

Neil Snowball is the executive director responsible for the Wellness programme in Europe. Together with his team, he has crafted a programme that integrates six elements: fitness, nutrition, work and family, health, learning and recreation. This translates into a number of staff support services and facilities, including fitness centres, medical and dental care units and a back-up childcare centre for when parents' usual arrangements fall through.

"There are very clear commercial goals behind the wellness programme," Snowball explains. "Attracting and retaining world-class people is an ongoing challenge and any competitive advantage that we can offer can often make a significant difference. The firm also acknowledges that people at Goldman Sachs do work hard and are very committed to us."

Employees pay subsidised fees for most services. This reduces the impact on the firm's bottom line and ensures that the programme is able to continue to support the needs of employees through all stages of the economic business cycle.

The Goldman Sachs Wellness team continue to monitor the business case around the wellness programme. "Any organisation planning to embark on a wellness-related initiative however large or small needs to understand clearly what it hopes to achieve and why," says Snowball.

"We've done work on the return on investment but this was not a driver at the outset," he continues. "If you provide critical support such as the childcare centre, it enables staff to continue functioning. We have a dentist on site and we know that without it many people wouldn't have their regular check up. It is classic preventative medicine. Our pay back is the reduction in sickness absence."

While 'general illness' remains the primary (and accepted) reason for absence, stress now appears in this category and is more prevalent among white collar workers as a reason for being off sick. Indeed, 'stress' is being increasingly used as a catch-all term in workplace health (see chapter 2). According to the Health and Safety Executive, about five million workers describe their job as 'very stressful', and around half a million say they experience work-related stress at levels that they believe make them ill.

DETERMINING THE CAUSE OF STRESS

Occupational health specialists prefer to talk about 'pressures' on people, as a way of examining the components that contribute to the overall stress problem in both individuals and groups of people. A problem could be complex and multi-factorial, or relatively simple to identify and rectify. Whatever the issues, stress is here to stay as the major cause of well being-related costs, from direct absenteeism to reduced productivity and creativity (see chapter 2).

Other major causes for concern are musculo-skeletal conditions – including back problems – and work-related upper limb disorders – a term that encompasses the older repetitive strain injury category (RSI).

For companies, a big worry is the threat of litigation, brought by people who have successfully claimed for compensation for ill health attributable to the workplace. There have been awards of hundreds of thousands of pounds to workers in the public sector for stress-related illness. (Cases in the private sector have been less frequent, as union representation tends to be less strong.)

Personal injury cases are heard in the courts, but employment tribunals also often reveal a health angle, such as where a bullying manager has led to a case of constructive dismissal.

The law is still being tested with regard to stress, but an important appeal court judgement in February 2002, which dismissed three of four successful tribunal cases, clarified a critical point for employers. The court ruled that if an organisation is exercising a reasonable duty of care towards its employees, it can only be held responsible for problems that are brought to its

TARGETS FOR CHANGE

One of the best ways companies can demonstrate their commitment to health and safety is to set themselves targets for change, says Roger Bibbings, Occupational Safety Adviser for the Royal Society for the Prevention of Accidents (RoSPA)

"Health and Safety needs to be seen as a business performance issue not just minimal compliance with regulations," he says. "Organisations need to ensure health and safety is recognised at director level as a clear priority and underpinned by full consultation and involvement – eg of trade union health and safety representatives."

While the government, campaigning groups such as RoSPA and enforcement bodies such as the Health and Safety Executive can offer companies support and guidance, the core effort must come from business itself. Individual organisations need to set effective corporate performance improvement targets at corporate, divisional and even departmental levels.

Target setting needs to be underpinned by a robust understanding of current performance status, including continuing problems and their causes and possible solutions. 'Headline' targets may need to be broken down and expressed in a form that is relevant to subsidiary levels in sectors or organisations.

Target setting in the area of health and safety needs to be understood in the context of an organisation's approach to target setting in general. In turn, this needs to be viewed in relation to its overall approach to decision making. Targets are most likely to be effective in leveraging change when they are 'evidence-based' and they are set with the active involvement of the groups or individuals who will be held accountable for delivering against them.

Increasingly it is being understood that occupational safety and health performance is multidimensional. No single measure such as lost-time injury rate provides an overriding indication of an organisation's success or failure in managing work-related risk. RoSPA believes that a more holistic approach to performance assessment is required.

More detailed guidance on measuring and reporting on corporate health and safety is contained in a document, Towards Best Practice which can be found in the Occupational Safety section of RoSPA's web site www.rospa.com under DASH – Director Action on Safety and Health. A companion document, Targets for Change, will be available in the near future.

attention. This means that it is the responsibility of the employee to bring, say, a stress problem that is related to workload to a manager's attention, if the problem was not reasonably foreseeable by management.

But employers need to identify and handle stress with the same due care as they avoid accidental, physical injury of employees. The court noted that companies that set up counselling services for employees may go some way towards providing a reasonable duty of care. Indeed, larger organisations are turning increasingly to the services of employee assistance programme (EAP) providers, which provide personal support for employees' health and wellbeing and, at corporate level, address those issues that contribute to generic ill-health, absenteeism and low productivity.

TAKING SAFETY SERIOUSLY

While much of today's emphasis is on health and wellbeing issues, government is continuing to view safety and work-related diseases very seriously. A visit to the HSE's web site reveals campaigns on construction and road safety, and August 2002 saw the start of the Control of the Asbestos at Work Regulations.

There are many health and safety issues that cross over into statutory responsibility, for example, the relationship between alcohol and workplace accidents, or between driving and long working hours. (A recent TUC report warned that employers are likely to face increasing problems related to drug and alcohol misuse by their workers. If ignored, the problem could cost UK industry £800m a year.)

But beyond statutory responsibility there is the wider question of an employer's role in supporting the government's aim for people to have greater choice and control over how they work. The Work-Life Balance campaign run by the DTI is a case in point, as are a range of health promotion activities designed to help people exercise more, eat healthier food in the canteen and cut down on smoking, drinking and drug-taking.

There are also productivity arguments for taking extra steps for creating a healthier, happier workforce. Many organisations do participate in health promotion activities, often networking with local health promotion specialists in health authorities and NHS trusts, as well as with health clubs, local authorities and other like-minded businesses. Larger organisations are more likely to run activities such as health fairs for employees, and also to offer screening and occupational health services.

While large organisations have the advantage of being able to dedicate resources to the battery of health and safety issues, regulations and guidance, the HSE has recently increased resources tailored to help smaller businesses, including materials that address areas that are more difficult to judge, such as stress.

Even so, a survey of nearly 5,000 employers, conducted by the Institute of Occupational Medicine (IOM) for the HSE, revealed that access to occupational health support is patchy for smaller companies. Only seven million of the UK's 25m workers – 30 per cent of the workforce – have access to occupational health services. (Ten years ago it was 50 per cent.) The IOM attributes the drop to an increasing number of smaller firms, and a perception that there are no 'relevant' hazards (although clearly many companies have inherent problems with stress, musculo-skeletal disorders and long working hours). Smaller companies that did provide an occupational health service, gave the main motive as the need to protect the health of the workforce. Other issues cited were concerns about litigation and the cost of sickness absence.

'Occupational health' in this context covers a wide spectrum of definitions and, as outlined above, there are a plethora of strategies, projects and networks relating to workplace health in the UK.

In the longer term, a major concern for society is chronic illness and absenteeism. Very few people on long-term sick leave return to work at present, placing an increasing load on resources available for incapacity benefit. With a workforce increasing in average age, rehabilitation will gain in importance for companies, and special issues, such as the workplace health needs of groups such as older women, will come to the fore.

Sponsor a Director's Guide

With more than 50 titles produced, the Director's Guide series is a highly successful business publishing venture

Each guide is produced in conjunction with a major blue-chip sponsor – from Oracle and KPMG to BT and Microsoft – and each is sent free to 50,000 individual members of the IoD in the UK.

Director's Guides cover a diverse range of topics – from e-commerce to growth finance, from customer care to management buy-outs. Research shows the series forms a key part of IoD members' business reading, with a high retention value and pass-on readership. The direct benefits to the sponsor include:

- *50,000 individual director-level circulation*
- *Strong position as an authority in its specialist area*
- *Authorship of three chapters*
- *Full co-branding with the IoD*
- *Seven pages of exclusive advertising, including two colour positions on the covers*
- *A reply-paid card bound into the guide, for direct response*
- *3,000 sponsor copies*
- *Broad press coverage*

For further enquiries, please contact
Business Development and Sponsorship on:
020 7766 8885
or e-mail us at busdev@iod.com

Chapter 2

Understanding workplace issues

In today's businesses there are fewer serious accidents, but more of us are suffering from long-term physical and mental conditions, says Paul Roberts, head of the HSE's Securing Health Together Unit

EXECUTIVE SUMMARY

- Stress and musculo-skeletal disorders are the two most common self-reported causes of worker ill-health and absenteeism.

- Evidence tells us that people who report problems with stress will also tend to report more musculo-skeletal problems, and vice versa.

- Increased sickness absence can have a domino effect on remaining workers, lowering morale, staff performance and productivity.

- Other types of work-related ill-health include asthma, deafness, and skin disease.

Not so many years ago most staff worked in large concerns. They were employed in physically active roles in traditional industries such as manufacturing, steel and coal. By contrast, the majority of today's workers are employed in small firms following big increases in the service sectors, desk jobs and the use of computers. Overall, competitive pressures and the demands on everyone are greater.

The nature of risk has also shifted. There are fewer major accidents, overall, but new risks have become important. This means that as well as preventing accidents, today's directors need to focus on ways to achieve a healthier workforce.

If there was a serious accident in your business today, you would soon know about it. Injured people would require medical attention, workmates would need to be comforted and relatives and the HSE to be informed.

At the very least, there would be an interruption to normal business and there could also be damage to equipment.

Later on, the company could be called on to answer questions from the media. There could also be investigations by the authorities leading to legal action.

LONG-TERM ILLNESS

Generally speaking, however, serious accidents are rare compared to the much larger number of people affected by mental and physical wellbeing issues. But do not assume that a lack of dramatic events means that all is well. In the interests of your business and your workforce, it is important that you understand and prevent ill health too.

Mental and physical health conditions are sometimes called 'slow accidents', because they can build up over a period of time. They're often caused by a number of factors, some of which may involve people's lives outside work. In some instances, the people affected do not take time off. Instead, they carry on for years, tense, unhappy, in pain and less productive professionally. (This is called 'presenteeism'.) Some also enter a negative spiral of abuse, using alcohol, tobacco and drugs in an attempt to cope.

COMMON CONDITIONS

The two issues most commonly associated with worker illness and absence are stress and musculo-skeletal disorders.

Musculo-skeletal Disorders (MSDs)

This term simply means damage to muscles, joints, tendons, nerves and ligaments. Such damage can be caused by work that imposes too great a strain on the body, such as lifting awkward or excessive loads. But it can also arise from low-strain but high tension body movements that are repeated time after time. Examples are use of a computer and mouse, or processing goods at supermarket checkouts, if the work area is not properly designed.

MSDs can occur in any industry. It is estimated that about 1.2m workers suffer musculo-skeletal disorders caused by their work, resulting in the loss of ten million working days per year (source: HSE self-reported work-related illness survey 1995).

The most common places on the body to be affected are the back and shoulders, and arms and hands. The warning signs are:

- *Workers' complaints of aches and pains;*

- *High sickness absence;*

- *Frequent rest stops;*

- *Makeshift improvements to workstations and tools (eg. seat padding);*

- *Use of bandages, copper bracelets, liniment, etc.*

DOs AND DON'Ts FOR BACK PAIN SUFFERERS

DO:

- Stay as active as possible, but see a doctor if you are worried or the pain persists or gets worse.

- Speak to the employer and discuss what can be done to help stay in work.

- Find out about back pain.

DON'T:

- Take to bed and wait for the pain to go away – the sooner you get back to normal activity the better.

- Worry – back pain is rarely serious and worrying delays recovery.

- Avoid activity simply as a way of avoiding the pain.

Stress

We all benefit from a reasonable degree of pressure and challenge, which can be stimulating. But in the context of health and safety, stress is defined as "the adverse reaction people have to excessive pressures or other types of demand placed on them". Work-related stress exists when people perceive that they cannot cope with what is being asked of them at work. In principle, everyone can be affected.

FEARSOME FACTS AND FIGURES

It's no surprise that violence, bullying and harassment are all causes of stress in the workplace. But to what extent do they pose a problem?

- A recent study on Violence at Work showed that people working in small businesses were more likely to be threatened or assaulted than those in larger organisations.

- Working directly with members of the public puts people at a higher risk of violence.

- The Chartered Institute of Personnel Development say that violence and bullying often goes unrecognised, and that:
  - One in eight UK employees had been bullied at work within a five-year period;
  - more than half those who had experienced bullying said it was commonplace in their organisation

- Bullying can take many forms involving the abuse of power, and may include racial and/or sexual harassment.

There are seven broad categories of risk for work-related stress:

- *Culture – of the organisation and how it approaches work-related stress;*

- *Demands – for example, workload and exposure to hazards;*

- *Control – how much say individuals have in the way they do their work;*

- *Relationships – including issues such as bullying and harassment (see box above);*

- *Change – how effectively organisational change is managed and communicated;*

- *Role – whether the individual understands his or her role in the organisation, and whether the organisation ensures that the individual does not have conflicting roles;*

- *Support, training and individual factors, including support from co-workers and managers, training and personal factors, such as personality and home life.*

STUDIES ON STRESS

The following is a summary of the key findings of two major studies conducting by the HSE on workplace stress

Bristol Stress and Health at Work Study
- One in five workers reported feeling very or extremely stressed by their work, equivalent to about five million workers in the UK;

- There was a link between reporting being very stressed and a range of job design factors, such as having too much work to do or not being supported by managers;

- Reports of high stress levels were also linked with a range of health outcomes, such as poor mental health and back pain; and health-related behaviours, such as drinking alcohol and smoking.

The Whitehall II Study
- Not having a say in how work is done is associated with poor mental health in men and a higher risk of alcohol dependence in women;

- Fast-paced work and the need to resolved conflicting priorities is linked with a higher risk of psychiatric disorder in both sexes, and poor physical fitness or illness in men;

- A combination of putting high effort into work and a poor recognition by managers is associated with increased risk of alcohol dependence in men, poor physical fitness or illness in women, and poor mental health in both sexes.

Remember, stress itself is not an illness, but if it is prolonged or particularly intense it may play a role in problems with heart disease, back pain and gastro-intestinal disturbances and mental conditions, such as anxiety and depression.

Stress and musculo-skeletal disorders are often associated with each other, ie. workers suffering from the effects of one may often be suffering from the other too.

IMPACT FOR BUSINESS

Work-related stress can lead to detrimental consequences for business, such as:

- *An increase in sickness absence, which can have a domino effect on remaining staff;*

■   *Reduced staff morale;*

■   *Reduced staff performance;*

■   *Staff seeking alternative employment, leaving the organisation with the expense of recruiting and training replacements.*

An estimated six-and-a-half million working days a year are lost through illnesses caused, or made worse by, work-related stress. People who take sick leave for stress are off for an average of 16 days, costing employers a total of around £370m every year.

OTHER TYPES OF WORK-RELATED ILL-HEALTH

There are other types of ill-health effects that may or may not be present depending on the type of work an individual does. Although this guide there is not space to do more than introduce them, they can cause serious health problems. They include:

■   *Skin diseases, eg. from exposure to solvents;*

■   *Asthma, eg. dermatitis, from contact with certain types of chemicals;*

■   *'Vibration white finger', eg. from use of some power tools;*

■   *Deafness, from exposure to noise;*

■   *Occupational cancer, from exposure to substances such as asbestos.*

Information and advice on dealing with such issues is available free on the HSE web site (see back of book).

Chapter 3

Benefiting from the right balance

Flexible working can be good for employees, good for families and good for business. The DTI's Best Practice at Work Team explains why

EXECUTIVE SUMMARY

- Traditional working patterns are incompatible with new business models.

- Flexibility may be the only way to retain certain key, experienced staff.

- Childcare facilities will help widen the recruitment and retention pool.

- Make life easier for your employees and they'll make life easier for you.

Ten years ago, the phrase 'work-life balance' was virtually unheard of. Today, it seems it is rarely out of the news. The move to business models built partly on the ideal of 24/7 customer service has revolutionised the workplace. Traditional working practices are no longer suitable for companies, their people, or their customers.

The workforce, too, is more diverse. Employees have greater responsibilities and commitments outside the workplace and look to their employers to provide opportunities to meet them. Employers can no longer expect working hours to fall into traditional, rigid patterns.

This holds particularly true for today's young professionals, who want a more balanced approach to work and place a greater emphasis on the need for wellbeing and a life 'of their own'. Ultimately, this generation will look to careers with employers that can deliver more than just a nine-to-five job and a pay cheque.

THE NEED

Parents with young children are often those who find it hardest to balance work and home life. From April 2003, employers will have a duty to consider applications to work flexibly from parents of children who are younger than six – younger than 18 if they are disabled. This important new right will stimulate and facilitate discussions at the workplace – hopefully, to the mutual satisfaction of both employees and companies.

Older employees nearing retirement may want gradually to reduce their hours in order to adapt slowly to a major lifestyle change. Some may want to work fewer hours in order to spend time with a partner who has retired. Faced with meeting continuing customer demands for good and experienced staff, the employer will want to accommodate them.

THE BUSINESS CASE

Despite these shifting expectations and cultural changes, there is still a lot of confusion about what work-life balance is. While some companies have embraced work-life balance practices and proved that policies can help solve common and costly business problems, many others have not acknowledged the benefits, let alone put practices in place.

When people are struggling to cope with the conflicting demands of work and non-work responsibilities, a toll is taken not only on their approach to work but also on their health and well-being. It has been estimated that stress-related absence costs industry £370m a year. Of course, 'stress' means different things to different people – from regularly working too many hours to simply having a bad day in the office – but a good and sensible employer will fulfil its legal responsibilities to provide a safe system of work and exercise its duty of care to its workforce. In this way, a preventative, rather than curative, approach can be taken to work-related stress.

Businesses of all shapes and sizes are operating in an increasingly competitive environment and are constantly faced with the need to increase productivity, lower staff turnover,

THE BUSINESS BENEFITS

- Attraction of the best talent.

- Retention of valued employees.

- Better client service.

- A return on investment in training.

- Reduction of absenteeism, sickness and stress.

- Improved productivity and performance.

- Increased morale, commitment and loyalty.

- Greater flexibility in staff attitudes; a culture that can adapt to change.

reduce absenteeism and optimise talent. Government research has shown that nine out of 10 employers believe people work best when they can balance work with the rest of their lives. This means that employers who fail to adopt work-life balance practices are potentially putting themselves at a competitive disadvantage.

CRACKS IN THE GLASS CEILING

Work-life balance policies can also help to address another problem experienced by a large number of UK companies – a lack of women in senior positions. The Equal Opportunities Commission has reported that men dominate in nine out of 11 managerial groups across all sectors, and that only one in ten company directors are female. Work-life balance practices can play a valuable role in reversing this trend.

With competition for skilled staff on the increase, it makes good commercial sense to widen the labour pool and retain the expertise of female staff by taking a more imaginative approach to the way we work.

Leading business names are rising to the challenge – and seeing the benefits. Before introducing its childcare programme, HSBC Bank used to lose 70 per cent of its staff who took maternity leave. Today, after 13 years of the nursery programme, it retains

85 per cent. Xerox says that better work-life balance practices over the past five years have dramatically improved staff retention levels in the UK, saving around £1m.

BT's Workstyle Consultancy Group estimates that flexible working arrangements can reduce absenteeism by 20-40 per cent and boost productivity by 20-40 per cent.

PARTNERSHIPS WITH PEOPLE

The business case for flexible working among SMEs is compelling. Research by the Institute of Employment Studies highlights the case of Automated Packaging Systems (UK), a small manufacturing company that took the decisive step of bringing together all of its informal flexible working patterns and introducing new practices such as 'banked hours' (see box opposite). The changes have delivered an absenteeism rate of only 1.5 per cent, high rates of staff retention and year-on-year growth in company turnover.

In all sizes of organisation, a key element in sustaining a productive and motivated workforce is the level of partnership and involvement between employer and employee. Indeed, partnership has been central to a government initiative encouraging employers, employees and their representatives to co-operate in solving particular business problems. The DTI Partnership at Work Fund is designed to spread best partnership practice more widely. Many organisations in the UK have realised the potential of a partnership approach to develop the productivity and job satisfaction of the workforce but there are still many others that are falling behind through their failure to change.

ENLIGHTENED SELF-INTEREST

The good news is that employers are increasingly recognising that a happy workforce is a productive workforce. Results from The Sunday Times 100 Best Companies to Work For Survey 2002 demonstrated that the most satisfied workers are those who feel they can choose working arrangements that suit their own lifestyles. Although some major companies in sectors other than retail can offer starting salaries that are more than five times that

THE WORKING PRACTICES

Work-life balance is not just about part-time working. It includes:

■ **Job sharing**
Two people jointly carry out the duties of a single job. Each person is employed part-time but together they cover a full-time post and divide the pay, holidays and other benefits.

■ **Staggered hours**
Employees have different start, finish and break times. Employers cover longer opening hours, while offering workers more flexibility.

■ **Term-time-only working**
Employees remain on a permanent contract, either on a full or part-time basis, but can have unpaid leave of absence during the school holidays.

■ **Flexi-time**
Giving people a choice about their actual working hours, usually outside agreed core times – allowing them to vary their starting and finishing times and sometimes also their break times during the day.

■ **Compressed hours**
People work a total number of agreed hours over a shorter number of working days.

■ **Annualised hours**
Employee work patterns are based on the number of hours to be worked over a year rather than a week. Particularly suitable for companies with cyclical workloads.

■ **Flexible working locations**
Staff work either at home or on the employers' premises.

■ **Practical employee benefits**
Childcare, health and fitness facilities and financial packages.

of full-time shop assistants, Asda tops the table when it comes to employee satisfaction. Employing nearly 120,000 people and with an annual turnover in full-time staff of only two per cent, the supermarket chain has demonstrated that it is possible to create a happy, motivated workforce while confronting the competitive challenges in today's marketplace. Its flexible practices include part-time working and offering older staff 'Benidorm leave' – a three-month unpaid winter break.

RAISING AWARENESS

With the launch of the DTI Work-Life Balance Campaign, the government is committed to raising awareness of the business case for work-life balance and to showing employers how they can implement the right policies in the workplace.

Through good employee consultation and choosing the right practices for the business, employers will realise the bottom-line benefits. The rationale is simple: employees who feel well and believe they have some control over the way they work, will be motivated to get out of bed in the morning.

Work-life balance doesn't mean we will be working less hard, or that none of us will ever work late ever again. It is about empowering employees with control and choice over their working lives, helping businesses to run more efficiently and ultimately, to boost productivity.

WORK IS PART OF LIFE

Ruth Lea, head of the IoD's Policy Unit, comments on the work-life balance debate

The IoD agrees with the DTI and others that extremes should be avoided. That is down to good management, and any good employer will recognise that a burned-out set of workers will not lead to long-term business success: apart from anything else, it can be very expensive to replace good employees. Flexibility, voluntarily negotiated, is to be encouraged. However, in reality, it is usually easier for larger organisations to introduce a range of initiatives than it is for smaller organisations.

For many people work is a fulfilling a part of life. And it can be a very rewarding part. Work provides income that may be used in an enormous variety of ways in the modern world, as compared with 50 years ago, for instance. Work contributes to the success of the economy as a whole (including the funding of public services), which is vital. Also, people in work tend to be healthier than those who happen to be out of work for one reason or another. This even gives rise to the term 'the healthy worker effect' in research on health and disease.

The IoD would prefer to speak of a 'work-leisure balance', or similar, so as to avoid any implication that work is not part of life.

Chapter 4

Managing sickness absence effectively

Occupational health experts are critical to the successful management of absence attributed to sickness, says Dr Robin Cox, independent consultant occupational physician

EXECUTIVE SUMMARY

- Occupational health advisers are critical to effective management of sickness absence.

- An OHA can liaise with an employee's own medical advisers and gain medical information, without breaching confidentiality.

- Early retirement should be considered in cases where sickness is prolonged or potentially irrevocable.

- In the future, more people will be employed beyond normal retirement age.

The management of absence attributed to sickness (AAS) is the responsibility of either a company's line management or personnel department. But, a company will only really succeed in controlling sickness absence if it has access to an occupational physician (OP), either directly or through an occupational health adviser (OHA).

Occupational Health (OH) is there to support the appropriate managers and to protect them and their employee from discrimination and misrepresentation or misinterpretation of the medical issues. An OP can also liaise with the employee's own medical advisers, obtaining medical information and reports as required and interpreting them for management without breaching confidentiality. The OP will also assume clinical and medico-legal responsibility for the company's occupational medical cases.

AAS is divided into two groups: short-term absence and long-term absence.

Short-term absence

This refers to periods of less than ten working days. They may be the result of minor medical conditions but often have no underlying medical cause.

It is important that short-term absence is measured in 'spells' of absence, rather than the total number of days absent. The implication of ten separate spells of absence totalling ten days in a six-month period is very different from a single spell of ten days in a similar period from influenza, for example.

If a company believes an employee has had an excessive amount of short-term absence the OP can determine whether there is any underlying medical cause and can also advise management if the underlying cause, medical or not, is work-related.

Long-term absence

This is any single period in excess of ten working days. There is usually a significant underlying medical reason for long-term absence. In such cases, the role of OH is to maintain liaison with the employee, to obtain all relevant medical information and to advise management on the prognosis. (This includes the expected duration of the illness, the implications for future work performance and any interventions that may hasten the patient's recovery and return to work.) OH will also advise on the employee's ultimate rehabilitation to the workplace.

Regular contact and encouragement from the company during periods of long-term absence is the key to expediting an employee's return to work. The message to be conveyed to the employee is:

- *You are a valuable member of the team and we want to see you at work;*

- *Your absence from the team impedes its performance;*

- *We will do all that we can to expedite your recovery and rehabilitate you to your workplace;*

- *We will take expert advice to ensure that everything is being done to assist your recovery and return to work.*

MODEL POLICY AND PROCEDURE

The following is a suggested model policy and procedure for the management of sickness absence at Twitchers plc, a fictitious firm

Policy

Twitchers wishes to reduce unplanned absence due to ill health. To that end the company wants to encourage healthy lifestyles and help employees who are absent through sickness to expedite their recovery and rehabilitation to the workplace. To achieve these objectives the company monitors sickness absence closely and utilises occupational health experts to the mutual benefit of itself and its employees.

Where deemed appropriate, Twitchers requires employees whose health problems are affecting their work or attendance to visit the company's occupational health adviser or occupational physician. The purpose of this is to obtain a report (excluding medically confidential data), regarding the employee's current and future fitness for employment.

Procedure

- Line managers record all sickness absence in their group.

- HR/Personnel collect, collate, analyse and monitor all sickness absence data.

- When certain trigger points have been reached, eg. five separate spells of absence in any six-month period or a single spell of more than ten days HR/Personnel will initiate actions as follows:

A. Short-term absence

If an employee cannot attend work through sickness he/she (or someone on their behalf) is required to notify his/her line manager or HR as early as possible on the first day of absence. HR will inform the line manager who will decide whether or not to interview the employee on his/her return. If an interview takes place it must be handled with sympathy, understanding and compassion, and the manager must be careful not to make any assumptions or accusations. It is a fact-finding interview, the purpose of which is to explain to the employee that their absence has been noticed, is regrettable, and that the company wishes to help them reduce it.

The manager must have a copy of the individual's sickness absence record at the meeting and a calendar with the sick days marked in red. This will make it easier to identify patterns, frequencies or coincidences in days taken off work. For example, they may coincide with school holidays, public holidays, annual leave, spouses or partner's annual leave, sporting fixtures, etc. The absence record should indicate clearly the number of work days lost through causes attributed to sickness, the number of spells of absence and the reasons given.

MODEL POLICY AND PROCEDURE

The manager should explore with the individual what lies behind the absence. Careful, persuasive and pertinent questions and answers should provide some clues. At the conclusion of the interview the reasons may be clear and the manager can agree with the employee an appropriate course of action. The gist of the interview and the action agreed must be documented and a copy given to the employee.

However, the employee may need to see the company's OP if one of the following apply: the manager suspects that the individual has a medical problem or problems; the individual admits to such problems or there is no clear explanation for the individual's repeated absences. Under these circumstances HR/Personnel should be asked to arrange an appointment.

The employee must be told that, in line with Twitcher's policy, such a referral will be arranged. The report which will follow the consultation with the OP will determine the further course of action.

B. Long-term absence

In these cases HR/Personnel should notify the occupational health adviser or OP as soon as the individual has been off work for 11 days. Depending on the accuracy and reliability of the information on the form the OHA /OP may respond in one or more of the following ways:

1. If the diagnosis is clear cut and the condition uncomplicated, the OHA /OP will be able to give personnel an immediate prognosis, with an estimated time of return to work and any rehabilitation that may be required.

2. The OHA /OP may need to obtain further information by contacting the patient, his/her GP or consultant before a prognosis can be given.

3. The OHA or the OP may need to see the patient at home (in cases of severe illness.)

In all cases the OHA will maintain regular contact with the patient and discuss his/her progress with the OP to ensure that the patient is receiving and complying with all appropriate care. The OP will also liaise with the patient's own medical attendants to ensure that there is no delay in his/her return to work.

Before returning to work the patient should be seen by the OHA or the OP so that the precise medical details of his/her condition can be recorded. This will ensure that a rehabilitation programme can be agreed and that any necessary modifications to his/her work or workplace can be discussed with HR/Personnel and line management and implemented in time for the employee's return.

EARLY RETIREMENT ON GROUNDS OF ILL HEALTH

When sickness is prolonged or apparently irrecoverable, premature retirement will need to be considered, either through a permanent health insurance carrier or by the employer invoking the option of ill health early retirement through its pension plan.

The patient will almost certainly be disabled as defined under the Disability Discrimination Act. The option of early retirement must, therefore, be justified against the alternative of making reasonable adjustment to the patient's work and working arrangements. If the company has permanent health insurance for cases of long-term disability, the decision of whether to accept an individual for benefit will rest with the insurer and its medical advisers. They will require medical evidence from the individual's GP or the company's occupational physician, or both.

If early retirement under the company's pension scheme is the preferred option the pension scheme trustees will require an independent medical assessment of the individual. It is strongly advised that this is provided by an independent occupational physician so as to avoid any suggestion that early retirement is being used as a 'redundancy exit'.

Any occupational physician who is asked to make an assessment for early retirement will require a copy of the rules of the pension plan. The criteria for medical retirement on medical grounds vary greatly from one pension plan to another.

Most pension plan rules were formulated before the medical advances of the last decades and, therefore, need to be reviewed. A condition that was considered 'permanent' a few years ago may now be treatable to the extent of prolonging working life to normal retirement age. Angina, for example, is no longer a permanent disability but a person suffering from it may be eligible for retirement under the rules of many pension plans, even if they have successful surgery. Another example is hip replacement surgery. Previously a person with severe osteoarthritis of the hip may have been permanently incapacitated long before the end of his normal working life. Now a successful new hip joint will enable him to go on working to normal retirement age.

COMPANY PROFILE: GO NORTH EAST

Ramona Nock, project co-ordinator at independent occupational health consultants Miller Health Management, and Stephanie Young, occupational health manager at public transport company Go North East, detail the implementation of an Attendance Management Policy at the company and the benefits it reaped

Go North East operates across 11 different sites and employs 2,200 staff (including 1,600 bus drivers). It has an onsite full-time occupational health manager, and an occupational physician who visits one day a week.

Identification of the problem
When the company conducted an occupational health audit it identified high levels of sickness absence and inconsistent ill-health retirement practices. As a result, absenteeism was identified as one of the five key focus areas for improvement in the Company's 2000/2001 business plan.

The audit findings were confirmed by Go North East's Occupational Health Manager (OHM) who found that:

■ there were no formal sickness absence procedures;

■ sickness absence was managed inconsistently across sites;

■ there was no mechanism to identify reasons for absence or computerised recording system.

Towards a solution
A Steering Group was assembled to develop an Attendance Management policy. The other objectives included:

■ raising the profile of health, safety and welfare;

■ improving the health status of employees by identifying sickness/absence issues/concerns;

■ reducing sickness/absence and the direct and indirect costs associated with these absences.

Before formulating a policy the Steering Group identified the current practice through a company-wide questionnaire, and undertook an analysis of best practice. This included:

■ reviewing best practice documents developed by organisations such as the Institute of Directors;

■ contacting occupational health professionals in other companies to obtain copies of their policies;

■ taking into consideration employment legislation which affect the policy (eg. Disability Discrimination Act 1995);

34

COMPANY PROFILE: GO NORTH EAST

The Draft Policy was presented to the Company Directors who approved the document. Line Managers and union representatives were also given an opportunity to review the policy and provided valuable input into issues surrounding implementation.

Implementation of the policy
Managers receive ongoing training on managing absence (eg. on triggers for referral to occupational health, return to work interviews, rehabilitation programme, self-referrals to occupational health). Employees were provided with briefing sheets with specific information on how the policy would affect them. They were also encouraged to review the entire policy.

Benefits
The absence rate at Go North East before the Attendance Management Policy was implemented was 5.8 per cent. Absence is currently 4.5 per cent, a reduction of 1.3 per cent. This has translated into considerable savings for the company.

OLDER PEOPLE AT WORK

Today, people's age expectancy is on the increase and many more of us are staying physically and mentally fit into what used to be regarded as 'old age'. These phenomena, coupled with the predicted increase in the need for experienced labour, will result in people being employed beyond normal retirement age.

There are many benefits in employing older people, not least being their long experience, accumulated skills and, usually, their dedication. But, it must also be borne in mind that, inevitably, there are some disadvantages in taking on older employees. These must be taken into account and suitable adjustment made. They include recognising that:

- *Chronic illness and disability becomes more common with advancing age;*

- *Older people are less adaptable than their younger colleagues;*

- *Older people take longer to learn new skills and find the acquisition of new skills more difficult;*

- *Physical strength declines with age;*

OLDER PEOPLE AT WORK

Companies that employ older workers should consider implementing the following policies and procedures:

- **Recruitment and selection**
  - raising the age limit on vacancies;
  - removing age limits;
  - offering temporary employment to older workers.

- **Training and career development**
  - developing specific training courses for older workers;
  - encouraging age-conscious personnel policies.

- **Flexibility**
  - improving the work environment and workload;
  - making adaptations to jobs.

- **Control of negative image-building**
  - conducting or reporting research on the good productivity of older workers;
  - conducting campaigns aimed at changing negative attitudes to ageing.

- **Changes in retirement policy**
  - raising the age of early retirement;
  - raising the mandatory retirement age.

- **Promote good health**
  - introducing no smoking policies and provide assistance to those who wish to stop smoking;
  - offering healthy diets in the canteen;
  - providing time and facilities for regular exercise;
  - enlisting professional help to provide a health education programme.

- *Visual and hearing acuities tend to decline with age;*

- *Physical fitness and general mobility tend to decline with age.*

However, healthy ageing will be promoted by meaningful and gainful employment along with determined attention to lifestyle factors such as avoiding smoking and obesity and maintaining regular physical exercise. All of these can be encouraged by appropriate programmes and policies within the workplace.

Chapter 5

The benefits of vocational rehabilitation

Vocational rehabilitation can greatly reduce sickness absence and increase productivity, says Dr Robin Cox, independent consultant occupational physician

EXECUTIVE SUMMARY

- Vocational rehabilitation focuses on the functional capability of an individual, rather than the medical diagnosis.

- There are occasions when an individual's state of health will not return to its pre-sickness/pre-injury level. Vocational rehabilitation can still ensure that employees return to working situations that are of benefit to themselves and their employers.

- A full Functional Capacity Assessment (FCA) may be required in cases where there's the potential for legal action.

To date, vocational rehabilitation has been sorely neglected as an option by companies that are attempting to return employees to work as expeditiously as possible after sickness or injury.

Historically, the reasons for this are the social security system, GPs' lack of knowledge of their patients' work and the inflexibility of employers. National Insurance certificates have only offered the choice of 'fit' or 'unfit' for work without any provision for a graduated return to work. GPs rarely have a detailed understanding of their patients' work or workplaces and no direct contact with their patients' employers. So, they're unable to advise on suitable rehabilitation programmes. Employers have been reluctant to make the required changes to the workplace and working hours for effective rehabilitation and employees have not embraced the opportunities that modern medicine and surgery offer for rapid recovery.

However, with the passage of the Disability Discrimination Act and the greater utilisation of occupational health professionals by employers, vocational rehabilitation is being recognised and utilised now as an alternative which can markedly reduce sickness absence and increase productivity.

ASSESSING FUNCTIONALITY

Vocational rehabilitation matches the present and expected functional capability of the individual to his/her work, workplace and the operational requirements of the employer. It is based on the functional capacity of the individual rather than the medical diagnosis. So, for example, although a hernia operation always used to require six weeks off work, an assessment can now identify to what extent an individual can lift, pull, push, walk, climb stairs, drive, etc. two days after a laparoscopic hernia repair. Such an assessment must also take into account the ability of the individual to get to and from work, since commuting is often a greater limiting factor in returning a person to work than the work itself.

A vocational rehabilitation assessment must be done by an occupational health professional, who has an intimate understanding of the employee's work and the operational requirements of the employer as well as an ability to assess the individual's functional capacity. The benefits of vocational rehabilitation are:

■   *To enable earlier return to work;*

■   *To limit disability payments;*

■   *To ensure earlier and more fully restored productivity.*

The occupational health professional performing the assessment must be aware of the individual's job description and must be able to undertake a job analysis which will identify and quantify the essential functions of the job in terms of:

■   *Basic physical demands – strength, endurance and range of movement (lifting, carrying, pushing and pulling);*

■   *Mobility requirements (walking and climbing);*

■ *Sensory and perceptual demands (hearing and vision);*

■ *Vocational requirements and environmental conditions such as exposure to heat, cold, vibration, etc.*

Employers are advised to obtain a vocational assessment at an early stage in the convalescence of any individual with an illness or injury, whose recovery is likely to take weeks rather than days. Such an assessment will determine a likely date of return to work; whether the individual will have any limitations; whether redeployment to alternative work may be necessary, temporarily or permanently; what adjustments may be needed either to the workplace or to the working hours; if and when the person is likely to be able to resume fully their normal work; whether there will be any long-term consequences from the condition; whether the individual has a disability within the definition of the Disability Discrimination Act; and any other pertinent but non-medically confidential information that the employer needs.

The prime objective of rehabilitation is to return injured or sick employees to their pre-morbid working status which is more cost-effective than paying long-term disability costs or hiring, training or transferring other workers to fill the post. Even so, it has to be recognised that, sometimes, return to 100 per cent normal functionality will not be achieved. In these cases, vocational assessment and rehabilitation will enable the reintegration of the employee to a working situation which is still mutually beneficial.

FULL FUNCTIONAL CAPACITY ASSESSMENT (FCA)

In some cases, especially those with potential legal consequences, a full functional capacity assessment (FCA) may be required. A FCA describes the evaluation of an employee in terms of their capacity to perform the essential duties of the job.

Standardised FCAs have been developed which use highly sophisticated apparatus that provides the referrer with high levels of objectivity, validity, reliability and predictability. The assessments are based on well-researched data and give an unbiased and independent evaluation of an individual's functional ability, not a diagnostic analysis of a specific illness or injury. Task requirements will dictate what part of the body is the main focus for the FCA. If a person lifts and carries, then the assessment will concentrate on the whole body but, for example, in the case of a secretary the focus may be more specifically on the upper extremities. Dynamic assessment of the whole body would take about four hours and follows strict protocols to evaluate up to 27 work-performance measures, including:

- *Walking/climbing;*

- *Standing/sitting;*

- *Lifting/carrying/repetitive hand and foot movements;*

- *Squatting/kneeling/crouching;*

- *Fine finger movements.*

By combining an analysis of torque patterns, variations in heart rate, pain behaviours and reports and physiological variables, the assessment can identify objectively the patient's level of ability and provide data on whether it is a genuine reflection of their current level. Employers receive a written report with measured quantifiable indices. In addition, a video recording of the patient's performance can be made and kept for permanent reference, future comparison and legal evidence.

Much of the information contained in this chapter has been taken from Fitness for Work (third edition), edited by R A F Cox and published by the Oxford University Press. The author is grateful to the contributors to this book, which also contains a comprehensive list of contacts and addresses of individuals and organisations that can provide advice and assistance on vocational assessment and rehabilitation.

Chapter 6

Formulating policy

How do you draw up a programme to promote employee wellbeing? And what should you cover? Paul Roberts, head of the HSE's Securing Health Together Unit, offers some guidelines

EXECUTIVE SUMMARY

- Make sure all managers and staff understand the rationale for health promotion.

- Identify and assess risks in order to set the right priorities.

- Review steps taken to mitigate risk and to 'educate' employees.

- Have clear policies on smoking and drink and drug abuse; follow the ILO code on HIV and AIDS.

The business case for health-promotion policies is well put in chapter 1. The arguments have as much to do with enlightened self-interest as paternalism and corporate social responsibility. Your employees are stakeholders in your business: to look after them is to look after yourself.

Here we focus on ways to formulate policies on employee health and give specific advice on policies covering smoking, alcohol and drug abuse, and HIV and AIDS.

GETTING STARTED

Health promotion does not necessarily require a big investment – in either money or time. Inexpensive leaflets and posters can help raise awareness of health issues. Free information and guidance is available on the internet from government web sites (see resources section). Trade or industry associations may also be able to help.

Your programme does not need to be run by managers: it could be delegated to an individual who has an interest in health and lifestyle issues. You many wish to take advice from an occupational health adviser, but this will not always be necessary to make effective progress.

Onsite health and fitness centres, employee assistance programmes and perks such as health club membership and subsidised 'rest-cure' holiday cottages are very nice. But none of them is compulsory.

GETTING BUY-IN

There may be cultural obstacles to health promotion. For example, some managers may feel that it smacks of 'nannying' or infringes on personal liberties.

It is therefore vital that you consult your colleagues and the workforce to ensure there is a supportive climate. Clearly communicate the rationale for the policy and stress that you are trying to provide people with the ability to make informed choices, not to limit personal freedom. Having a clear leader will make the communications exercise easier.

THE FIRST STEPS
Identifying and assessing risks

Certain health risks may be of more relevance to your business, or to your sector. To identify these you could:

■ *Hold informal discussions and 'walk throughs' to get a feel for people's jobs and how they relate to health.*

■ *Use performance appraisals for one-to-one discussions on health and lifestyle issues.*

■ *Use focus groups to find out what specific groups of people think.*

■ *Use 'managing attendance' interviews, which follow up on periods of absence, to talk about health problems. If staff do not wish to share concerns with their line managers, give them the option of talking to an occupational health adviser.*

■ *Check sickness absence data: high levels of sick leave may indicate problems; information about the causes may help to identify priorities. (Remember, however, that people do not always give the real reasons for absences.)*

■ *Check productivity data: a drop could mean health problems.*

■ *Check staff turnover: an increase could indicate health risks.*

■ *Use a confidential questionnaire – but take expert advice on how to frame the questions.*

It will not be necessary to undertake all of these exercises. But a combination of at least some of them will help you decide what areas to concentrate on. Whatever your chosen method, record your findings and your reasonable interpretation.

Setting priorities and targets

Priorities will be decided by a number of factors, including:

■ *incidence of particular conditions;*

■ *number of days lost;*

■ *degree of concern expressed;*

■ *performance measures such as staff turnover;*

■ *benefits of improvements;*

■ *costs of improvements.*

Once your priorities are known, you can set realistic targets for improvement. National improvement targets are based on the first two criteria, so use of these may help you later to compare and evaluate your achievements.

DEVELOPING THE PROGRAMME

To work, your plans must be supported by a procedural framework. This will mean establishing straightforward policies for dealing with health at work and establishing channels of communication on health matters. It could also usefully involve forming partnerships with other local businesses, a trade association, local Chambers of Commerce, or occupational health providers to help you deliver improvements.

Once the structure is in place, you can start to take action. What you do will depend on your individual circumstances and on the results of the risk identification and assessment process. The possibilities include: additional training for managers or other staff; campaigns to raise awareness; changes to job specifications and the working environment; the provision of counselling services and relaxation facilities. You may want to focus on healthier lifestyles through exercise, diet and realistic working hours.

MONITORING AND REVIEW

Once a policy has been implemented you cannot afford to sit back. You need to review:

■ *whether the steps taken have been successful;*

■ *what costs and benefits apply;*

■ *what other pros and cons there may be;*

■ *what changes (if any) to the programme are needed.*

Remember, risks change as staff members and working conditions do, so stage reviews periodically.

BEHAVIOURAL RISKS

Tackling risks that arise from employee behaviour is, perhaps, the area of health and safety that employers find most difficult and most contentious. It must, however, be confronted. The behaviour of individuals affects others – co-workers, customers, suppliers and members of the public.

The company's approach must be responsible but not draconian or judgmental. There are likely to be underlying causes for the behaviour – work-related stress may be one.

Smoking

It is widely believed that tobacco smoking causes cancer and heart disease. It also has acute irritant effects on the eyes, throat and respiratory tract, and can increase symptoms of asthma. Both the smoker and those around him or her are at risk.

Smoking should be tackled directly. It is advisable to:

- *Have a clear policy – and a system to deal with breaches of it;*

- *Ensure that the policy is known to existing staff, visitors and job applicants;*

- *Make non-smoking the norm in enclosed workplaces;*

- *Make special provisions for smokers;*

- *Segregate smokers from non-smokers;*

- *Encourage smokers to give up – most local environmental health units and ASH (Action on Smoking and Health) should be able to provide help and advice.*

Alcohol and drug abuse

Drink and drug abuse can impair performance at work and be a serious threat to health and safety. It can also disrupt work and working relationships.

The objectives of your policy should be to:

- *Ensure that the misuse of alcohol, drugs (whether illegal, prescribed or obtained 'over the counter') or solvents does not impair the safe and efficient running of the organisation or put staff, contractor staff or the general public at risk.*

- *Encourage those who may have a problem to seek help.*

- *Ensure that staff comply with all relevant legal requirements, in particular the Health and Safety at Work Act 1974, the Misuse of Drugs Act 1971 and the Road Traffic Act 1988.*

The principles of your policy should be that:

- *The organisation will not accept the excessive or inappropriate use of alcohol, the misuse of drugs – whether illegal or prescribed – or the misuse of solvents.*

- *The first instance of alcohol and/or drug dependency or solvent abuse will be treated as a medical problem requiring special treatment and help, which may be supported by the employer.*

■ *Health education will be given to staff to reduce the likelihood of drink, drug or solvent misuse; and that managers will be given help to identify and deal with problems.*

■ *Staff going back to work after treatment will return to normal duties but that the organisation will respond as sympathetically as possible to requests for changes to working patterns to help reduce the risk of future problems.*

■ *Staff who feel they have a problem should be encouraged to seek help as a matter of urgency, either privately or through the organisation.*

■ *Cases will be treated in the strictest confidence and within the limits of what is practicable and lawful.*

The written policy should also explain the circumstances in which disciplinary procedures would be invoked.

HIV AND AIDS: A CODE OF PRACTICE

The International Labour Organisation (ILO) has drawn up best-practice guidelines for dealing with HIV and AIDS in the workplace. The following is a summary:

■ Care and support
Solidarity, care and support should guide the response to AIDS at the workplace. All workers are entitled to affordable health services and to benefits from statutory and occupational schemes.

■ Confidentiality
Access to personal data relating to a worker's HIV status should be bound by the rules of confidentiality consistent with existing ILO codes of practice.

■ Continuing the employment relationship
HIV infection is not a cause for termination of employment. Persons with HIV-related illnesses should be able to work for as long as medically fit in appropriate conditions.

■ **Gender equality**
More equal gender relations and the empowerment of women are vital to preventing the spread of HIV infection and enabling women to cope with HIV/AIDS.

HIV AND AIDS: A CODE OF PRACTICE

■ **Healthy work environment**
The work environment should be healthy and safe, and adapted to the state of health and capabilities of workers.

■ **Non-discrimination**
There should be no discrimination or stigmatisation against workers on the basis of real or perceived HIV status.

■ **Recognition of HIV/AIDS as a workplace issue**
HIV/AIDS is a workplace issue, not only because it affects the workforce, but also because the workplace can play a vital role in limiting the spread and effects of the epidemic.

■ Prevention
The social partners are in a unique position to promote prevention efforts through information and education, and to support changes in attitudes and behaviour.

■ **Screening for purposes of employment**
HIV/AIDS screening should not be required of job applicants or persons in employment, and testing for HIV should not be carried out at the workplace except as specified in this code.

■ **Social dialogue**
A successful HIV/AIDS policy and programme requires co-operation and trust and dialogue between employers, workers and governments.

Chapter 7

Choosing the right method of support

Employers can access a host of support services to ensure that their employees' health and happiness is optimised. Dr Kit Harling, director of NHS Plus, reports

EXECUTIVE SUMMARY

- Health promotion campaigns cannot deliver instant health improvements, but will lead to an improved sense of wellbeing among staff.

- The counselling industry has experienced huge growth as fewer people have friends and family to turn to in times of need.

- Employee assistance programmes offer staff instant access to general counselling and guidance on more dedicated sources of help.

- Health screening programmes, in general, are not 100 per cent reliable or accurate.

The relationship between health and work goes two ways. Work activities and exposures can cause illness or injury to the employee. Equally, employees' state of health will affect their ability to work, irrespective of the origin of the disease. Under health and safety legislation, it is a statutory requirement for employers to provide the necessary assistance to prevent staff being made ill by their work. But, as discussed in other chapters, it also makes good business sense to help employees to maintain good health and functionality. This chapter explores the options.

HEALTH PROMOTION CAMPAIGNS
Chronic ill health (morbidity) and the conditions that lead to premature death during working age are often caused by our way of life. Relative lack of exercise, too much tobacco and alcohol and a diet of convenience foods are major contributors to ill health.

These factors take effect over very long periods of time; the foundation of some illnesses is laid in the eating and exercise habits of young children. Reversing these factors, through health and lifestyle interventions takes many years to have an effect.

Corporate health promotion campaigns, then, will not provide direct and immediate improvements in health. However, what they can do is to produce an improved sense of wellbeing and perception of general health among the workforce. In addition to the health benefits to the individual, there is likely to be a business improvement.

This was first documented by professor Elton Mayo in the 1930s. During experiments into productivity and working conditions at the Western Electric Hawthorne Works in Chicago, he discovered that productivity increased when employees' conditions were improved. The productivity increased further when adverse physical conditions were reduced.

The Hawthorne Effect still holds true for today, demonstrating the complex interactions at work and the benefits enjoyed by employers that take a visible interest in their employees' health, wellbeing and conditions.

The Department of Health organises health-promoting campaigns, as do many voluntary groups that deal with specific conditions. Employers wishing to introduce health and lifestyle programmes may find it easier to piggy-back these campaigns than attempting to establish their own.

COUNSELLING

In the last two decades, we've witnessed a huge growth in the counselling industry. In parallel there has been a proliferation of meanings given to the term 'counselling'. At one end of the spectrum, it is the name given to a practitioner who provides no advice, but listens to an individual recount their problems and encourages them to explore their own solutions. At the opposite end, the term refers to a formal therapeutic intervention used to treat psychiatric illness. In the context of this guide, we are using the first definition.

In today's world many people have little time to sit and reflect on their life. Hectic lifestyles and the demise of the nuclear family mean that many people have fewer friends and relatives to whom they can turn in times of difficulty. The ability to take 'time out' and explore life problems with a non-judgmental counsellor, in a non-threatening and entirely confidential environment, is hugely beneficial.

Finding a suitable counsellor can appear daunting, but The British Association of Counselling and Psychotherapy can provide a list of its members in a particular area. All of its members have to comply with a code of practice which is essential to effective counselling. Groups of counsellors are available and may be particularly useful for employers that have more than one site (www.bac.co.uk).

EMPLOYEE ASSISTANCE PROGRAMMES

These programmes started in the US but have been operating in the UK for many years. Research shows a clear financial benefit to employers who offer their workforce access to these programmes.

In essence, employee assistance programmes are a larger and more complex system of counselling. They usually provide 24-hour phone access for immediate assistance, which is followed up with a number of face-to-face counselling sessions. Often an employee's family will also be able to use the service.

In addition to direct counselling, the programmes provide detailed information and signposting for other dedicated services that could benefit the individual more than general counselling. As a result, they represent a first port-of-call for people who are struggling with housing problems, debt, relationship troubles and legal issues.

So far, research suggests that only 20 per cent of calls to employee assistance programmes relate to workplace difficulties directly. Nonetheless, to employers, the remaining 80 per cent of calls that relate to problems outside of work are equally important, since these external worries often impact on an employee's attendance, productivity and quality of work.

SCREENING AND PREVENTATIVE HEALTHCARE

Barely a week goes by without the popular press extolling the virtues of one or other health-screening programme. In a world besotted with technological fixes, the idea of using a simple measurement to detect an abnormality and correct the problem seems to promise great benefits for the individual. However, in practice, this promise is rarely fulfilled.

By definition, screening attempts to identify problems that could occur in the future by making a measurement in the present. Inevitably, screening takes place on otherwise fit and healthy individuals. These tests are neither perfectly sensitive nor specific. Some people who will go on to develop the illness will have a negative screening test and, by the same token, some whose health will be unimpaired in the future will have a positive screening test. This is inherent in the science of screening tests and does not represent error or mistake in conducting the tests. (For mathematical reasons the likelihood of these unintended outcomes is greater in populations of well people.)

The impact of being told, incorrectly, that you will develop a serious illness in the future is easy to imagine. At best it will result in worrying and unpleasant investigation. Equally, the damage to result from false reassurance of future health is obvious.

Some screening programmes have been rigorously evaluated. The two best-known examples are cervical screening and mammography, both of which have national programmes under the NHS. These programmes have been shown to produce a net benefit for the population.

The same can be said for the measuring of blood pressure and the testing of urine for the presence of sugar to determine whether an individual is in the early stages of diabetes. These tests are routinely carried out by GPs, but are also commonly undertaken in industry. There is very clear evidence that having raised blood pressure is associated with an increased risk of heart attack or stroke in the future. There is also clear evidence that reducing blood pressure reduces the likelihood of these devastating illnesses.

In the last few years there has been an increasing interest in health surveillance. Such techniques are a statutory requirement where employees are exposed to certain hazards at work, but now more companies are conducting a general surveillance of the health of the workforce. As yet, there is little evidence to confirm that this benefits either the company or the individual.

There are also intriguing ethical questions as to what extent an employee may legitimately intervene in the life and health of their employees' outside work activities.

PROVIDING INFORMATION

Over the last ten years there has been an explosion in the amount of health information available to both employers and employees. One consequence of this has been the variable quality of that information. It is now extremely cheap and simple to access health information on the internet, but what is difficult is being able to discern whether the material on view represents main stream opinion or the view of a determined individual. Worse still, the internet has also allowed quacks, charlatans and snake-oil sellers of old to move into the 21st century.

The NHS is committed to providing clear, concise, quality information to all. NHS Direct is a telephone helpline that offers health information directly to the public. NHS Direct Online provides the same information electronically.

CONCLUSION

On occasion, however, an employer will need more direct help from health experts. NHS Plus and many commercial organisations sell services to employers. These range from individual specialist practitioners or small partnerships through to large health organisations with a nationwide network of qualified practitioners.

In many circumstances the provision of information and assistance for employees is a statutory duty. But this is only is part of the story. Businesses that provide assistance to the workforce and help individuals to achieve their full potential, will be rewarded with improved productivity and attendance levels.

Chapter 8

Minimising health and safety hazards

Lawrence Waterman, senior member of the Institution of Occupational Safety and Health (IOSH) and managing director of Sypol, a leading HS&E consultancy, identifies some common threats to health and safety at work

EXECUTIVE SUMMARY

■ Risks must be identified and assessed and their management closely monitored.

■ Repetitive strain injuries can be avoided by paying closer attention to working environments.

■ Clear health and safety guidelines must be issued to employees who drive as part of their jobs.

■ Stress levels can be reduced by reviewing practices and re-organising management structures.

This chapter focuses on the practicalities of health and safety risk management. It looks at some specific hazards and at ways to eliminate or reduce them.

THE PRINCIPLES

Common, fundamental principles underlie any successful risk-management strategy. They are:

■ *Risk management is a key responsibility for directors. (See the following chapter.) The help of professional advisers is needed in order to discharge it fully.*

■ *Risks can only be managed if hazards are properly identified.*

■ *Risk identification is a continuous process. New working practices and changes to the way the company operates will bring new risks: the 'hazards at work' list must be kept up-to-date.*

■ *The size of each risk has to be assessed – resources should be allocated according to a list of priorities.*

■ *Precautions must be proportionate to the harm that could arise, ranging from complete avoidance to mitigation (see 'hierarchy of controls' below).*

■ *Whatever the risks and the precautions, staff need to know about them and be trained to work safely.*

■ *Risk management strategy needs to be monitored and periodically reviewed to ensure that it is working effectively and that adequate controls have been put in place.*

HIERARCHY OF CONTROLS

■ **Eliminate risks**
Use safer alternatives or avoid the process.

■ **Combat risks (at source)**
Use engineering controls and give collective protective measures priority.

■ **Minimise risks**
Design suitable systems of working and use personal protective clothing and equipment only as a last resort.

Source: HSE's guidance HSG65

THE PRACTICE

Risk management is based on the following imperatives: 'plan; do; check: act'.

Planning involves spotting the hazards and assessing the risks. It also involves deciding on the controls and establishing staff responsibilities and accountabilities. These will typically be defined in the health and safety policy statement signed by the chief executive, managing director or chairman.

'Do' means doing what you have decided is necessary. Checking involves monitoring, auditing, reviewing – processes that result in directors being clear about what is going on within the organisation. Action is required when the checking identifies opportunities for further improvements.

The plan, do, check, act cycle keeps the company moving forward to ever-lower levels of accidents and work-related illnesses. It effectively tightens the directors' grip on the organisation.

SPECIFIC RISKS

Work-related upper limb disorders (WRULDs) and Musculo-skeletal Disorders (MSDs)

Musculo-skeletal strains and sprains are the commonest type of work-related injury. Complaints of musculo-skeletal pain and fatigue are more common when tasks are repetitive and operators are tense. The solution may include providing breaks and rest periods, as well as making, ergonomic adjustments to the working environment. Consider the following example:

A company employing 40 staff working at computer screens and keyboards all day had failed to pay sufficient attention to working practices. After a visit from an inspector, it decided to get some professional help. A health and safety adviser ran three short (one-hour) training sessions. Each employee was asked to attend one of the sessions and then to go back and assess their own workstation using a simple checklist and form. The form was emailed back to the adviser and checked. Some of the staff were then visited by the adviser to sort out any problems. Three days and a few window blinds, document holders and footrests later, the workforce was much happier and, arguably, more productive.

With a simple exercise that caused little disruption to the working day, the company had fulfilled its legal obligations.

Driver fatigue

Driver fatigue is a very serious problem. Sleepiness reduces reaction time, vigilance, alertness and concentration, and causes many thousands of accidents a year.

A study conducted in the UK between 1987 and 1992 found that 16 per cent of all road accidents and 23 per cent of all motorway accidents were sleep-related. Research by the Transport

Road Laboratory found slightly lower proportions of sleep-related accidents: nine to ten per cent of accidents on all roads, and 15 per cent of accidents on motorways. In this study, though, 29 per cent of drivers reported having felt close to falling asleep at the wheel at least once in the previous 12 months.

Sleep-related accidents tend to be more severe, possibly because of the higher speeds involved and because the driver is unable to take any avoiding action, or even brake, before collision.

Young male drivers, truck drivers, company car drivers and shift workers are most likely to fall asleep while driving, but anyone driving long distances or when they're tired is a high risk.

The early hours of the morning and the middle of the after-noon are the peak times for fatigue-related accidents.

It is clear that many types of drivers at work have driving patterns that are associated with sleep-related accidents. Therefore, employers must make the management of risks surrounding job-related driving an active part of their health and safety policy.

Principally, they should:

■ *Manage the safety of employees who drive as part of their jobs.*

■ *Consider and implement the most suitable system of risk assessment for the road-safety needs of the company and its employees.*

■ *Choose the right vehicle and the safest specification for the needs of the job.*

■ *Ensure that work schedules and appointments enable drivers to stay within the law.*

■ *Provide sensible guidelines on driving and the use of vehicles for all employees who drive – or may drive – for the company.*

Stress

All over the world, work-related stress is a topical issue. According to recent reports:

■ *In the UK, more than 40m working days are lost each year due to stress-related absence.*

■ *In Australia, the federal assistant minister for industrial relations put the cost of occupational stress at around A$30m in 1994.*

■ *In the US, more than half of the 550m working days lost to absenteeism each year are stress-related.*

Stress has implications for workplace safety as well as employee wellbeing. Excessive workloads or unrealistic time constraints might make employees feel tempted to take short-cuts that compromise safety standards (eg. overriding machine guards) in an attempt to save time and achieve output targets. Where employees are subject to management bullying (another factor that causes stress) they might be hesitant to raise health and safety concerns, and so increase the likelihood of accidents.

Stress management has traditionally focused on individual approaches, usually by counselling individuals or small groups of employees on ways to adapt to, or cope with, various occupational stressors and/or their consequences. However, safety professionals now argue the case for adapting the work environment to the abilities and needs of workers. This could involve a thorough review of working practices. (See case study, below.)

CASE STUDY: BUS COMPANIES

Bus drivers have a worse sickness record than other comparable workers. The average age of those leaving their jobs for medical reasons is young, relative to similar groups

Their main health problems are pains in the back, tendons and joints, mental disorders and cardiovascular diseases. The driver's cab is constrained and the seat often lacks sufficient adjustability.

Mental-health problems arise primarily from the constant need to cope with conflicting demands. The company and the public want the driver to maintain good contact with passengers and to be service-oriented – for example, by providing information to passengers on timetables, routes, fares, etc. But they also want him/her to keep to a tight schedule in dense traffic. A further demand, which may clash with the previous two, is the need to drive safely, according to traffic regulations and conditions.

CASE STUDY: BUS COMPANIES

It is becoming more and more likely that bus drivers, in common with all types of transport staff, will be subject to threats and violence from passengers. Add to this the fact that work schedules and shifts put strains on family life and you have a potential occupational-health disaster.

In a case such as this, risk management would cover:

■ The ergonomics of the driver's cabin, with particular reference to the position and adjustability of the seat, the steering wheel and the pedals, and the visibility and marking of the dashboard. Provision should be made for adequate driver training, especially when new bus models are introduced.

■ Timetables, shift schedules and the quality of break periods. Limitations would be put on weekly and daily working hours, and adequate numbers of breaks and rest periods allowed. The other key issues would be: the organisation of work into shift 'blocks' of several consecutive days, combined with the forward rotation of shifts (early shift, followed by day shift, followed by late shift); the avoidance of split shifts (whereby drivers would be required to work a few hours in the early morning, followed by several hours in the evening); and the provision of two days off, rather than single days off, between shift 'blocks'.

■ Management style. Driving staff would be divided into a number of groups (of between ten and 20) with a supervisor and system of work consultation for each group. Supervisors and managers would be trained in a supportive style of leadership, which would include a proper information flow and clear explanations as to why certain things are or are not possible.

Provision would be made for training and retraining, and for special facilities for older drivers and drivers with health problems. Rehabilitation and individual work-resumption plans would be offered to drivers returning to work following health problems. A programme to prevent problems related to threats and violence would also be necessary.

Chapter 9

Health risk management

PART ONE: THE THEORY

Risk management is about choice and optimisation. Failure to allow for predictable losses or under-performances can be just as disastrous as overcompensating for them, says Dr Andrew Auty, principal consultant at the BRE

EXECUTIVE SUMMARY

■ Health risk is a function of the probability and severity of an adverse outcome involving health.

■ Damage to the health of employees, customers and people affected by environmental risks equals damage to a company's reputation.

■ Companies must decide what level of exposure to risk they can tolerate.

■ Each type of risk must be identified and evaluated before it can be managed.

Business risks come in many shapes and sizes. Most companies know how to manage contract risks, investment risks, marketing risks, etc., but how many understand health risks? How many know what the choices are, or how much they cost?

DEFINING RISK

Before discussing the options, it is useful to define risk in a way that applies to health risks, irrespective of origin.

Health risk is a function of the probability and severity of an adverse outcome involving health. Examples would include:

■ *causing (or failing to prevent) an injury which keeps someone off work;*

- *a high workload, making it difficult for people to return to work following sickness absence;*

- *work that is uncomfortable for all but the very fit.*

By definition what we are describing is a pure risk. Pure risks are not about speculative risks such as a fortunate stock market investment, or hiring inexperienced but promising talent. They are all about loss, its prevention and containment.

Losses due to ill health are inevitable but their frequency and magnitude can be managed.

Our starting point in business planning is usually, and quite naturally, the assumption of robust or adequate health of people at work. Management's objective is to manage any downward variation from this and minimise its effects on key business parameters.

Using this definition of risk and the usual business planning model above, the best we can hope for is that the cost of reducing these risks are matched by resulting savings/reduced losses.

Health risk management is also about optimising your 'health resource'. This resource can be measured as the number of fully effective working days provided by your workforce in each year. Someone who is under par will not be as effective (profitable after investment) as someone who is fully fit.

We also have to acknowledge that some losses due to health problems are inevitable and that, given this, optimisation of profits will always be less than maximisation of profits. Of course, there are interventions such as health promotion, which start from the more realistic assumption that everyone's health can be improved or risks minimised. Examples are:

- *offering an appropriate annual flu vaccination;*

- *providing healthy eating options in the canteen;*

- *introducing an anti-smoking policy;*

- *subsidising membership of gyms and sports clubs;*

- *incentivising people to cycle or walk to work or meetings.*

WHAT IS THE BOTTOM-LINE IMPACT?

Much as we may wish to manage risks for humanitarian or altruistic reasons, all pure risks, if they are realised, will ultimately be measured against profit.

Costs of ill health are either direct or indirect. All will affect the bottom line, but direct costs are easier to include in the business plan (see table below).

Some direct costs are compulsory, either because the law requires them or shareholders demand them to protect their investment. In other instances they relate to employee incentives and benefits that boost staff recruitment and retention.

Damage to reputation is particularly influential in risk management decision making. Damage to the health of employees, customers and people affected by environmental risks, are certain to damage company reputation.

COSTS OF ILL HEALTH	
Direct costs	**Indirect costs**
■ Statutory sick pay	■ Increased risk of accidents
■ Occupational sick pay	■ Unwanted staff turnover
■ Pension payments	■ Lost or delayed production
■ Administration	■ Inability to provide timely service to customers
■ Overtime	■ Damage to company reputation
■ National Insurance contributions	
■ Risk retention costs	■ Increased production or service costs
■ Employer's liability (EL), Public liabilities (PL) etc. insurances	■ Higher staffing levels
	■ Shortages of (skilled) labour
■ Prevention, mitigation costs	■ Extra recruitment and training costs
■ Compensation and legal costs	
■ Damage to property	■ Low staff morale

WHAT ARE THE CHOICES?

Many companies are so focused on managing demanding clients, uncertain suppliers, critical support services, etc. that they leave little time for health risk management. As a result, most react to health-related losses rather than plan for them. But it is vital that a company understands its health risk management choices, if it is to make decisions that suit its particular circumstances.

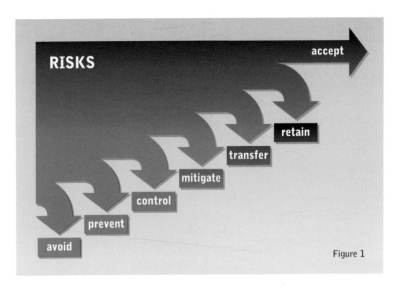

RISKS

accept

retain

transfer

mitigate

control

prevent

avoid

Figure 1

Figure 1 above displays a series of management options, each of which has an effect on final exposure to risk (the right end of the arrow). Each option has implications for the optimisation of the health resource and the availability of assets. In general, the aim is to reduce the significance of unassessed or unmanaged exposure to risk. The choices are:

Accept the risk

This is the most passive form of risk management. Once chosen, the risk requires no further investment of time or money. Risks which are accepted include those of which you are unaware and those which you do know of but accept there is nothing to be done about (eg. risks from exposure to asbestos were once accepted).

Retain the risk

Prepare for the worst or most likely outcome in your current business plan by setting aside the resources required to meet the loss. Clearly, there is a risk that the loss may never happen, in which case the contingency plan has been wasted in real terms. But you still have the assets and may have benefited from the reassurance.

Transfer the risk

If a risk can be measured in financial terms and it's in the public interest to do so, you can insure against it. In this case, the only retained risks are the premium (assets remain out of reach unless you cancel the policy), policy excesses and uninsured costs. This still carries the risk that loss may never occur and the asset tied up in the premium cannot be recovered once the policy period expires.

Mitigate

Once a loss event has begun, it may be possible to 'spend to save'. For example:

- *If a key employee needs an operation and NHS waiting lists are long, it may be worth investing in private medical care.*

- *If a type of working results in unusually high reporting of back pain problems and absence, it may be worth investing in ways to make the work more comfortable.*

Control

If you know losses are to be expected through ill health, you can reduce your exposure to risk through control by, for example, 'multi-skilling' employees.

Prevention

Knowing that a health condition is likely and is subject to your intervention, gives you the option of preventing it. Generally speaking, this is the arena of occupational health.

Avoidance

Halting the line of business or activity can be the most drastic option in risk management. However, from time to time it must be considered, ie. if a specific activity has a history of costly ill health it may be more economic to sell it off or simply close it down.

HOW DO YOU CHOOSE?

Directors must start the process by identifying and evaluating each form of risk before deciding how to manage it.

Evaluation includes an assessment of the effect and effectiveness of each of the risk management choices illustrated by Figure 1. Done well, this can be a very complex task.

Prescribed choices

Ill health which is caused or made worse by work must be risk-assessed by law, and prioritised for avoidance or prevention, so far as is reasonably practicable. Insurance for the compensation of employees whose ill health is caused or made worse by work is also a legal requirement. A key point is that occupational cause or aggravation of ill health accounts for less than 16 per cent of health-related absence from work.

Historical precedent

Although larger companies can, to a great extent, rely on historical data to estimate direct costs going forward, such information is often incomplete and inaccurate. Even for large companies, history will not have explored all the health risks that might present in the coming period.

Scenario planning

It is worth considering the health risks that were not manifest in the past and to try to estimate their significance if they were to occur. Investors would be reassured if this approach was adopted.

This approach might also be the only option for small companies with no records to refer to. A Political Economic Social and Technological (PEST) analysis of worst case scenarios will quickly tell you whether or not you are in a position to take the risk. Analysis of the risk management options (see Figure 1) will usually reveal that you have already invested in measures that will reduce the probability or potential severity of loss.

PART TWO: VIEW FROM THE TOP

Lawrence Waterman, senior member of the Institution of Occupational Safety and Health (IOSH) and managing director of Sypol, a leading HS&E consultancy, sets out the practical implications of safety management

EXECUTIVE SUMMARY

■ Effective safety management underpins high staff morale, low turnover and sustainability.

■ Employers and staff need to identify and discuss those hazards that are intrinsic to their line of work.

■ With careful planning many hazards can be eliminated; the rest can be managed.

Good safety management enhances business performance; poor safety threatens survival in competitive environments.

Take a typical work area – an office, warehouse or workshop. In this scenario, everything is a mess: there are materials and equipment lying across walkways, trailing cables, a broken light creating a dark corner. Could anyone expect that such an area is run like clockwork by a manager who's so committed that the quality of the work and the efficiency of the team is maintained at all times? Clearly not. We all know what good management looks like – even when it is hard to define. Managing safety properly contributes to good management, high staff morale and low turnover, and sustainable operations.

ESSENTIAL ELEMENTS OF SAFETY
Knowing the risks
The new guidance on corporate governance, and requirements such as the Combined Code (Turnbull) for listed companies, have made UK companies aware that being a director means managing risk. Some of the risks will be financial, others to reputation or to market share from competitors.

THE IOSH APPROACH TO OCCUPATIONAL HEALTH

Effective management of occupational health is crucial to the health of individuals, businesses and society as a whole, says the Institution of Occupational Safety and Health (IOSH), Europe's leading body representing occupational safety and health professionals

"Employers should not regard occupational health (OH) services as optional extras, but rather as 'essential enablers' to the smooth and efficient running of their businesses," says Richard Jones, head of Technical Affairs at IOSH.

As for individual businesses, IOSH argues that OH risk should be managed as part of the overall business risk management, with all employees being involved. Small to medium-sized enterprises (SMEs), it stresses, are particularly vulnerable, as the absence of a key employee can result in the failure to meet contractual commitments.

In order to promote the business risk management approach, IOSH has worked on a European project to develop a web-based Risk Management Toolkit for SMEs (see www.iosh.co.uk/technical). Information is also available for business start-ups at www.safestartup.org.

IOSH believes that owners/managing directors are key to effective OH management. In 2000, it was estimated that as many as one in three EU employees suffered from work-related stress. This is symptomatic of organisational failure – eg. a culture that accepts excessive working hours; bullying and harassment; or poor management of change – and not of individual weakness.

Organisational leaders set the tone and ethos of their companies and should recognise the value of good OH practice in helping to ensure that, in the words of Revitalising Health and Safety, they have a workforce that is "happy, healthy and here".

Furthermore, the workplace can be used by employers to promote the 'healthier living' message, with the aim of improving the quality of life of their employees, as well as improving performance. Increasingly, directors are seeking ways to embrace the principles of corporate social responsibility (CSR). To this end, some larger companies are providing subsidised OH services to their supply-chain companies, thereby also increasing their suppliers' reliability and reducing business risk.

In 2000, a MORI poll on consumer attitudes to CSR in 12 European countries, showed that 77 per cent of respondents ranked 'protecting the health and safety of workers' as the most important area for companies to contribute to or support.

One area of risk is health and safety. This can threaten normal operations, such as a major fire in a factory, or can have a chronic effect as it becomes harder to keep staff in a workplace perceived as unsafe or unhealthy.

Employers need to think about the hazards intrinsic to a type of work and discuss these with staff. Within every sector there are risks that form part of what needs to be managed. Offices may have trip hazards, electrical equipment, access routes, computers, etc. Factories can have hazardous substances, machinery, fire hazards, manual handling, noise, etc. Outdoor workers have to cope with roads, sunlight, threats of violence, aggression, etc.

Knowing how to manage the risks

There are practical ways of managing hazards to workers and others. They can be prevented altogether with some forethought. For example, using water-based paints to decorate premises, will eliminate the need to suffer the smells and toxic vapours from solvent-based paints. Or, perhaps working practices can be improved by, for example, providing warehouse staff with small trolleys to handle paper deliveries rather than expecting them to carry heavy boxes of paper. If all else fails, staff may need to be given individual protection, such as supplying site engineers with ear muffs when they enter a noisy plant room.

Legal compliance – as a minimum

Some risks will be subject to a company's own assessment of what needs to be done to give effective protection to its people. But in other cases, legislation dictates minimum standards that have to be met. Hearing defenders may be a good idea in many circumstances, but above a certain level of noise exposure they are mandatory. Whatever risks a company has to manage, it must check the minimum standards required by law.

Knowing how you well you're doing

Those who direct and manage know that deciding what to do is only a small part of the job – getting it implemented and checking that it is working are the critical elements. The same is true of health and safety, where it is crucial to set performance indicators and check on progress.

It's an ongoing commitment

The effort to reduce and eliminate accidents and ill health is never over. Companies need to keep looking for the next opportunity to improve performance. The most effective way to do this is to implement an annual business planning cycle that includes setting health and safety targets – not just for outcomes such as reduced accident rates but also for inputs such as training efforts. Carrying out an annual health and safety review is the same discipline as carrying out the annual audit and annual budget setting.

THE PROFESSIONAL HEALTH AND SAFETY ADVISOR

This programme of managing risk – from hazard spotting to annual review – can appear daunting. How can a director know that all the significant hazards have been identified, that the company is not going overboard on risk management or missing something legally required?

At least part of the answer lies in getting professional support. The law makes clear that employers must provide directors and managers with competent health and safety assistance (Regulation 7, Management of Health and Safety at Work Regulations 1999). So any questions about putting a health and safety programme in place should be directed to a qualified advisor.

KEEPING A SENSE OF PROPORTION

'Reasonably practicable' is a horrible piece of health and safety jargon that means no more than putting in effort which matches the risk. No company would run a week's training at a country hotel in order to help office staff avoid suffering paper cuts but neither would an employer hesitate to authorise extensive training for its window cleaners who need to abseil from the top of shopping centres. The tables on the opposite page are taken from BS8800:1996 (published by the BSI). They show how to define the level of risk and also a risk-based control plan.

ASSESSING THE LEVEL OF RISK

	SLIGHTLY HARMFUL	HARMFUL	EXTREMELY HARMFUL
Highly unlikely	Trivial risk	Tolerable risk	Moderate risk
Unlikely	Tolerable risk	Moderate risk	Substantial risk
Likely	Moderate risk	Substantial risk	Intolerable risk

WHAT ACTION IS REQUIRED?

RISK LEVEL	ACTION AND TIMESCALE
Trivial	No action is required and no documentary records need to be kept.
Tolerable	No additional controls are required. Consideration may be given to a more cost-effective solution or improvement that imposes no additional cost burden. Monitoring is required to ensure that the controls are maintained.
Moderate	Efforts should be made to reduce the risk, but the costs of prevention should be carefully measured and limited. Risk reduction measures should be implemented within a defined time period. Where the moderate risk is associated with extremely harmful consequences, further assessment may be necessary to establish more precisely the likelihood of harm as a basis for determining the need for improved control measures.
Substantial	Work should not be started until the risk has been reduced. Considerable resources may have to be allocated to reduce the risk. Where the risk involves work in progress, urgent action should be taken.
Intolerable	Work should not be started or continued until the risk has been reduced. If it is not possible to reduce the risk, even with unlimited resources, work has to remain prohibited.

It is because much of the health and safety programme is based on judgements such as these that many directors have found formal management systems, akin to quality's ISO 9000, so useful.

Chapter 10

Risk transfer

Insurance is an important part of health and safety risk management. Dr Andrew Auty, principal consultant at the BRE, looks at the policies on offer

EXECUTIVE SUMMARY

■ A 'one-size-fits-all' approach will backfire; seek advice about what cover best suits your needs.

■ Some policies provide access to occupational health services and programmes to rehabilitate employees.

■ Group schemes and limited-cover options help cut insurance costs.

■ Employers' liability insurance is a statutory requirement.

The management of health risks has been described in depth in chapter 9. Risk management choices are many and varied, but key among them is risk transfer – the option of paying someone else to bear all or part of the financial cost of your loss. Risk transfer is better known as insurance.

Insurance cannot cover you against everything. Losses that remain uninsured are retained by you. In general, the more risk you retain, the more you will have to invest in risk management procedures. The right balance of risk transfer and risk retention will depend on a business's individual circumstances.

This chapter gives a broad outline of health-related insurance policies. You, or your risk manager, or your broker will be able to negotiate policy variations as necessary.

OCCUPATIONAL HEALTH SERVICES

Some insurers provide access to occupational health services in return for an annual fee. The cost should be well below that of employing a full-time company doctor.

Services include:

■ *referrals to an occupational health physician;*

■ *vaccinations;*

■ *pre-employment medical screening;*

■ *information lines;*

■ *health and safety consulting;*

■ *occupational health screening;*

■ *health and safety bulletins.*

PRIVATE MEDICAL INSURANCE (PMI)

Private medical insurance is designed to cover treatment for curable, short-term illness or injury and is arranged for one year at a time. It provides the reassurance of knowing that treatment is available promptly, enabling an employer to better manage employee absence. Different policies will cover different illnesses and treatments. Typical exclusions include:

■ *drug abuse;*

■ *self-inflicted injuries;*

■ *injuries arising from dangerous hobbies or hazardous pursuits;*

■ *HIV/AIDS;*

■ *war risks;*

■ *kidney dialysis;*

■ *organ transplant;*

■ *infertility;*

■ *obstetrics (when the pregnancy is low-risk);*

■ *cosmetic surgery;*

■ *gender reassignment;*

■ *mobility aids;*

■ *drugs and dressings administered in out-patient care;*

- *preventive treatment;*

- *experimental treatment.*

Some insurers offer the cheaper option of providing care only when the employee's ability to carry out their usual duties is affected.

INCOME PROTECTION (IP)

Income protection, also known as permanent health insurance, enables businesses to provide a guaranteed income for employees who are unable to work as a result of illness or injury. The insurer is likely to require evidence that the claimant is unable to follow his/her normal occupation.

Cover is usually up to 75 per cent of pre-event remuneration. Benefit payments continue until the employee's recovery, death, or the termination of the insured period (normally retirement age), whichever occurs first. In addition, the policy will usually continue to pay a proportion of the benefit for an employee who returns to work either in a part-time or reduced capacity.

There is normally a waiting period before IP policies pay out – during which time the employer may be paying the employee a high proportion of his pre-event remuneration. The longer the period before the insured benefit starts, the lower the premium but the higher the unproductive salary costs. The minimum waiting period is around three months – but can go to 104 weeks.

IP insurers have a vested interest in employees' return to work, and it is increasingly common to find rehabilitation services included in the policy.

CRITICAL ILLNESS

Critical illness insurance provides a sum of money in the event of an employee becoming critically ill or undergoing a serious operation. Critical illness policies usually pay a tax-free lump sum if you suffer from one of the illnesses or conditions, or undergo one of the surgical procedures, covered. The list under PMI (above) provides a rough guide to exclusions. By purchasing group policies, a company can make considerable savings.

DEATH IN SERVICE

Group life cover enables employers to provide dependants of a deceased employee with ongoing support. This type of employee benefit ranks as a business expense, so premiums enjoy valuable tax relief. You are free to select any level of benefit for your employees up to the maximum allowed by the Inland Revenue. Typical benefits are:

- *a tax-free lump sum of four times annual earnings at the date of death;*

- *a dependant's pension of up to 4/9ths of annual earnings at the date of death.*

Group schemes are often available for 10 or more employees.

PERSONAL ACCIDENT

This type of policy pays a regular cash benefit to a person unable to work as a result of an accident or sickness. It is particularly suitable for the self-employed, who have no company sickness benefits. Personal accident policies are arranged for one year and are renewable at the discretion of the insurer. Regular weekly payments are usually made to the sick or injured, up to a maximum number of weeks (typically, 52 or 104).

There will normally be a deferred period (such as seven days) before payments start.

LIABILITY

Liability insurances generally include provision for legal expenses, but you should confirm the extent and scope of such cover in each particular case.

Public liability (PL)

If your negligence causes or aggravates harm to non-employees they may sue you for compensation.

PL insurance is optional and the level of cover provided is up to you. The more you expect to pay in the event of an injury, the more cover you will need.

Standard tests of negligence are:

- *Was a duty of care owed?*

- *Was the duty of care breached?*

- *Was the harm being claimed for a foreseeable consequence of a breach of duty?*

- *Was the harm being claimed for actually caused by the breach of duty in question?*

Exclusions and warranties are common in PL policies. Your insurer will want to see evidence that you are controlling risks to your contractors and the public.

Employers' liability (EL)

This is a compulsory insurance for all UK employers (with the exception of the Crown and similar employers). You can be fined heavily for each day you trade without EL cover.

The purpose of EL is to ensure that employers, even if they have long since gone out of business, have access to money that can be used to pay compensation to employees who are injured or made ill as a result of employer negligence.

The employee sues the employer and has the burden of proving the case; the insurer pays the bill if the claim succeeds.

The money paid to the employee is in the form of an indemnity, ie. its purpose is to return the employee to the position they would have been in but for the accident.

The standards used to determine whether the employer was negligent are those of the civil law. Such standards are continually under review. Official guidance (from the EC or HSE) also carries some weight when making an assessment of negligence. Official standards increasingly tend to adopt a precautionary approach.

The amount of cover provided is limited to £5m per loss event. But, as you have no idea in advance just how serious any single event will be there is very little relationship between premium paid and cover provided. Exclusions, which could put the access to funds in jeopardy, are forbidden by law.

Insurers have very little control other than to require high premiums when they are not satisfied with existing prevention measures, or to refuse to renew or write a policy. If your company or trade sector has a very poor claims history you must expect to pay higher premiums. If your insurer is very concerned by your recent history it may refuse to renew the policy.

Increasingly, EL insurers are becoming involved with mitigation of loss where liability is clear cut from an early stage. They generally use the term rehabilitation to describe this mitigation activity. Its main aims are to speed up access to post-acute healthcare (where this would be beneficial), to encourage active recovery and to increase opportunities for an early return to work.

Typical claims are for harm caused by: slips and trips; collisions; falls from heights; extreme vibration; noise; allergens. EL insurers quite often provide a free survey of your working systems with advice on means for controlling risks.

Claims for 'stress' continue to increase rapidly but the proportion of those that fail is also rising: the overall cost is less than half a per cent of the annual EL bill.

Products liability

Products liability insurance is a specific form of public liability insurance. If your product causes harm to your customers or anyone who could reasonably have expected to be harmed (eg. a guest of your customer) you may be liable for damages. Typical claims are for harm caused by: poisoning; exposed sharp edges; electric shocks.

The harm to your company's reputation may be much more significant than the cost of a claim. Many companies insure the cost of product recall – not necessarily to protect against a spreading of claims activity but to reassure the public that they are taking a responsible, precautionary approach.

Chapter 11

Looking to the future

The coming years will see directors and their companies coping with expanding responsibilities for occupational health and safety issues. Howard Fidderman, editor, Health and Safety Bulletin, reports

EXECUTIVE SUMMARY

- Directors could face prosecution in relation to a new charge of corporate killing, if current Home Office proposals are accepted.

- Employers will have to comply with significant new duties.

- Trade unions, insurers and the courts are all likely to play greater roles in tackling occupational safety and health.

The next few years will see directors and senior managers becoming involved in occupational safety and health (OSH) in a way that few have been previously. The government, the Health and Safety Commission (HSC) and its Executive (HSE) have each made it clear that they expect OSH to be a boardroom issue.

This view is expressed most explicitly in the HSC's 2001 booklet on *Directors' Responsibilities for Health and Safety*, but it also underpins the Home Office's current proposals for a new offence of corporate killing, as well as the recent increase in prosecutions of directors under section 37 of the Health and Safety at Work Act 1974 (HSW).

The importance of boardroom involvement runs through the two government and HSC/E strategies for improving OSH over the current decade, *Revitalising Health and Safety* and *Securing Health Together*. These landmark documents set targets for reductions in injuries and ill health by 2010 and action points to help their realisation (see chapter 1). The strategies build on the success of the regime introduced by the HSW Act. But they also reflect the need for additional approaches and 'levers' to protect the health and safety of the 21st century workforce.

THE MAIN DRIVERS

Although the roles of employers and the HSC/E will remain pivotal, these strategies highlight the importance of involvement from other institutions. The first-term Labour government saw environment minister Michael Meacher and deputy prime minister John Prescott build on their commitments in opposition to become the most interventionist and positive safety ministers since 1974. The *Securing* and *Revitalising* blueprints were established, and the HSE has pursued the non-legislative action points with confidence and vigour. The second-term administration, however, with Meacher and Prescott elsewhere engaged, has appeared less committed, and most of the legislative commitments of *Revitalising* remain unimplemented. Indeed, the period since 1997 has paradoxically seen less new significant legislation than under the previous Conservative administrations.

The European Commission – an object of hate for so many employers in the 1990s with its 'six-pack' Directives – is unlikely to provoke such passion again. Its plan of work until 2006 finds it short on new ideas, but keen to consolidate implementation and enforcement of its existing legislative portfolio. This can only benefit the UK, which traditionally has adopted a 'fight hard, implement honestly' approach to EU Directives. Other member states may have more to fear. The Commission promises new legislation on ergonomics, display screen equipment and carcinogens, but action on 'new' hazards such as psychological harassment and violence at work will, at least initially, be restricted to a non-legislative 'communication'.

But lest anyone think the Commission has gone quiet, the next year will see HSC proposals for implementing recent or imminent European Directives on falls from height, working time in the transport sector, vibration, noise (which might widen audiometry requirements for employers) and asbestos.

Three further institutions are set to play major roles this decade:

- *Trade unions – a mainstay of the health and safety system – are set to increase their influence via partnership initiatives.*

- *Insurers are expected to play a greater role in OSH. The HSC/E believe the industry is an under-tapped resource that could secure higher standards through premia setting, advice and rehabilitation – much as it does in mainland Europe.*

- *Courts should follow the Court of Appeal and Magistrates Association sentencing guidelines and increase the severity of their sanctions against employers convicted of OSH breaches.*

LENGTHENING THE ARM OF THE LAW

Some of the anticipated legislative and quasi-legislative developments are listed in the box on pages 78 and 79. Most attention, however, is currently focused on two draft Bills that, together, will constitute the biggest OSH shake-up since the implementation of the six-pack Directives in 1992.

The first would replace the law of manslaughter with an offence of corporate killing and two individual offences of reckless and gross carelessness killing, under which directors could also be prosecuted. Although organisations would be the primary target, directors could also face fines, disqualification and, perhaps, even a prison term. Progress has stalled since public consultation ended in 2000, but successive Home Office ministers have confirmed their commitment to introducing the Bill. The Bill is also a Labour election manifesto commitment, and so difficult to ignore.

The second Bill is a major piece of legislation that will, on a day-to-day basis affect more employers. Again this has been delayed, but the government remains committed to introducing it, subject to parliamentary time. The Safety Bill at Work will:

- *Increase the penalties available to magistrates for health and safety offences.*

- *Increase the number of OSH offences for which a person can go to prison.*

- *Implement other* Revitalising *recommendations.*

- *Amend the HSW Act to reflect the changing nature of work and afford the same protection to all workers, regardless of employment status.*

- *Set a framework for delivery of the government's commitments on road safety.*

- *Remove Crown immunity from statutory enforcement.*

- *May amend the HSW Act to enable private prosecutions without the consent of the Director of Public Prosecutions.*

THINGS TO COME

In addition to the safety and corporate killing Bills, employers will need to keep up with the developing health, safey and welfare regime

Annual reports The UK's top 350 private sector companies should have included health and safety in their 2001/02 annual reports. From 2004, this 'voluntary' information will be expected of all organisations with more than 250 employees. The HSE will monitor the response before looking at how to expand the reporting requirements.

Asbestos New Regulations on the control of asbestos are due to be laid in autumn 2002. They will include a new duty to manage asbestos in buildings, although this will not come into force until March 2004.

Chemicals The chemical agents Directive is due to be implemented in the UK in autumn 2002. This involves the replacement of Regulations on hazardous substances (COSHH) and lead, new Regulations on explosive atmospheres, and an Approved Code of Practice on asthma.

Civil liability Late 2002 should see amendments to the Management of Health and Safety at Work Regulations and the Fire Precautions (Workplace) Regulations that will allow employers and employees to be sued for breach of either set of the Regulations. The change will largely reflect common law duties and is unlikely to have a major impact.

Fire After a decade of false starts, the government has committed itself to having a unified and simplified fire safety regime in place by late 2003. The change will involve the consolidation of 120 pieces of legislation into a risk assessment-based set of Regulations. Consultation on the government's proposals will end in November 2002.

THINGS TO COME

Investigation The next few months are likely to see Regulations before Parliament placing an explicit legal duty on employers to carry out investigations into accidents and injuries at work.

NHS costs Consultation will end in November 2002 on a government proposal that would allow the NHS to recover its hospital and ambulance costs in all cases where a person has received personal injury compensation for an accident or illness, including those that are related to work. The government estimates this will increase an average Employer's Liability insurance premium by five and seven per cent.

Passive smoking Consultation closed on a draft ACoP in October 1999 that would require employers to introduce a smoking policy and consider a ban on smoking in the workplace. Although the HSC recommended an ACoP in September 2000, the HSE is currently reviewing the main stumbling blocks – the hospitality and small business sectors – and advises that there will be developments, albeit not necessarily this year.

Roads As early as 2004, employers will be expected to adopt a risk-assessment approach to the management of at-work road safety, and integrate it into their workplace OSH management systems. This is likely to be realised mainly through guidance, rather than legislative change.

Safety representatives This autumn will see a major HSE consultation exercise on harmonising the different sets of Regulations that govern the provision of information to, and the participation and representation of, employees. Also, a pilot HSE scheme is underway involving 'roving' union reps visiting non-unionised workplaces in five industrial sectors.

Stress In 2003, the HSE will publish standards for measuring employers' performance in preventing work-related stress. The standards will facilitate enforcement of stress-related offences and are likely to lead to the development of an Approved Code of Practice on stress.

BENEFITS FOR ALL

Legislative compliance aside, those directors who embrace the *Revitalised* world are likely to see their companies benefit financially from higher standards of health and safety, increased profitability and reductions in insurance premia, personal injury claims, absence and lost production. Enforcement will always be with us, but the current decade for the enlightened employer will be characterised by partnership and the integration of OSH into other disciplines and areas of business management.

Government, HSE and legislation web sites/publications

'Directors' responsibilities for health and safety': www.hse.gov.uk/pubns/indg343.pdf

'Revitalising health and safety', strategy and progress reports: www.hse.gov.uk/revitalising/index.htm

'Securing health together', strategy and progress reports: www.ohstrategy.net

'Adapting to change in work and society: a new Community strategy on health and safety at work 2002–2006', Commission of the European Communities, 11 March 2002, COM(2002)118 final.

Free and priced HSE publications are available from HSE Books, PO Box 1999, Sudbury, Suffolk CO10 2WA, tel: 01787 881165, fax: 01787 313995, www.hsebooks.co.uk. Priced publications may be obtained through booksellers.

HSE website: www.hse.gov.uk; note that the Health and Safety Commission and Health and Safety Executive are now under the remit of the Department for Work and Pensions (www.dwp.gov.uk)

UK legislation: The Stationery Office, PO Box 276, London SW8 5DT, tel: 0870 6005522, website: www.legislation.hmso.gov.uk

EU legislation: The Official Journal, Stationery Office, International Sales Agency, 51 Nine Elms Lane, London SW8 5OR, tel: 020 7873 8463.

Health and Safety Commission consultative documents are available at: www.hse.gov.uk/condocs

HSE contract research reports are also available free at: www.hse.gov.uk/research/content/crr/index.htm

Free advice on health and safety is available from HSE InfoLine, tel: 08701 545500, fax: 02920 859260, email: hseinformationservices@natbrit.com, or HSE Information Services, Caerphilly Business Park, Caerphilly CF83 3GG.

NHS Plus is part of the NHS contribution to the ten-year Occupational Health Strategy to improve the provision of occupational health support to all employers and employees with a particular focus on small and medium sized enterprises. It is a network of 115 OH departments in England which provides services to non-NHS employers. The web site provides information focused on occupational health issues and allows the enquirer to locate their nearest NHS Occupational Health Service. Tel: 0800 092 0062; www.nhsplus.nhs.uk

The Healthy Workplace Initiative (www.signupweb.net) is is jointly sponsored by the Department of Health and the Health and Safety Executive. The site includes information on the back in Work back care campaign.

The Managing Absence website (www.managingabsence.org.uk), has advice on costing and reducing sickness absence.

The DTI has set up a Work-Life Balance campaign site at www.dti.gov.uk/work-lifebalance; see also www.dti.gov.uk/partnershipfund, www.employersforwork-life balance.org.uk; www.worklifebalancecentre.org and www.tuc.org.uk/changingtimes

Regional sites

Health Education Board for Scotland. www.hebs.com
Scotland's Health at Work: www.shaw.uk.com
Promoting Health and Wellbeing in Wales www.hpw.wales.gov.uk

Employer bodies

Among the health-related publications produced by the CBI is the annual absence and labour turnover survey (www.cbi.org.uk).

The Institute of Directors (www.iod.co.uk), British Chamber of Commerce (www.britishchambers.org.uk), Federation of Small Business (www.fsb.org.uk) are other good sources of data.

Trade unions

Most large trade unions produce valuable health and safety information. The TUC produces an excellent weekly Risks bulletin on health and safety. Visit www.tuc.org.uk

Commercial providers

Many companies provide services such as stress auditing and employee assistance programmes. Among them are Businesshealth, which provides fortnightly digests of workplace health news (www.businesshealth.co.uk). Others include Turning Point (www.turningpointuk.com); New Ways to Work (www.new-ways.co.uk)

SINGLE ISSUE AGENCIES WITH WORKPLACE/ EMPLOYER INITIATIVES

Accidents

Royal Society for the Prevention of Accidents: www.rospa.co.uk

Alcohol

Alcohol Concern: www.alcoholconcern.org.uk
Institute of Alcohol Studies: www.ias.org.uk

Asthma

National Asthma Campaign: www.asthma.org.uk

Back pain

BackCare: www.backpain.org
Campaign for Better Seating: www.betterseating.org

Bullying

Bully Online: www.successunlimited.co.uk
Workplace Bullying: www.workplacebullying.com

Drugs

Department of Health: www.doh.gov.uk/drugs
National Drugs Helpline: www.nationaldrugshelpline.co.uk
Cross-government website: www.drugs.gov.uk

Flu and flu immunisation

Department of Health: www.doh.gov.uk/flu.htm
Public Health Laboratory Service: www.phls.co.uk/topics_az/influenza/flu.htm

Heart health

British Heart Foundation: www.bhf.org.uk
National Heart Forum: www.heartforum.org.uk

HIV/AIDS

National AIDS Trust: www.nat.org.uk

RSI

Repetitive Strain Injury Association:
www.rsi.org.uk

Smoking

Action on Smoking and Health: www.ash.org.uk
NHS Giving up smoking site: www.givingupsmoking.co.uk

Stress and mental health

International Stress Management Association: www.isma.org.uk
Mental Health Foundation www.mhf.org.uk
UK National Work-Stress Network: www.workstress.net

PROFESSIONAL BODIES

Association of British Insurers, 51 Gresham Street, London, EC2V 7HQ.
Tel: 020 7600 3333; www.abi.org.uk

Association of Occupational Health Nurse Practitioners (UK), PO Box 11785,
Peterhead AB42 5YG. Tel/Fax: 0116 281 3720; www.aohnp.co.uk

British Association for Counselling and Psychotherapy, 1 Regent Place, Rugby,
Warwickshire CV21 2PJ. Tel: 0870 443 5252; www.bac.co.uk

British Chiropractic Association, Blagrave House, 17 Blagrave Street, Reading,
Berkshire RG1 1QB. Tel: 0118 950 5950; www.chiropractic-uk.co.uk

Chartered Institute of Personnel and Development, CIPD House, Camp Road,
Wimbledon, London SW19 4UX. Tel: 020 8971 9000; www.cipd.co.uk

Employee Assistance Professionals Association, Premier House, 85 High Steet,
Witney, OXON OX8 6LY. Tel: 0800 783 7616; www.eapa.org.uk

Institution of Occupational Safety and Health, The Grange, Highfield Drive,
Wigston, Leicestershire LE18 1NN. Tel: 0116 257 3100; www.iosh.co.uk

Society of Occupational Medicine, 6 St Andrew's Place, Regent's Park, London
NW1 4LB. Tel: 020 7486 2641; www.som.org.uk

The Ergonomics Society, Devonshire House, Devonshire Square, Loughborough
LE11 3DW. Tel: 01509 234904; www.ergonomics.org.uk

ABOUT THE SPONSORS

The Association of British Insurers

The Association of British Insurers represents around 400 insurance companies, which between them account for over 97 per cent of the business of UK insurance companies. The Association represents insurance companies to the government and to regulatory and other agencies and provides a wide range of services to members.

The Department of Trade and Industry

The Department of Trade and Industry (DTI) works with businesses, employees and consumers to drive up UK productivity and competitiveness to deliver prosperity for all.

Activities include regulation, help and guidance, along with best practice schemes and initiatives, designed to facilitate sustained growth and productivity in the modern economy.

The Health and Safety Executive

HSE's mission is to ensure that risks to people's health and safety from work activities are properly controlled. Activities include enforcing good standards (usually by advising people on how to comply with the law, but sometimes by ordering them to make improvements and, if necessary, by prosecuting them); developing new health and safety standards; publishing guidance and advice; and providing an information service.

The Institution of Occupational Safety and Health

IOSH is Europe's leading body for individuals with professional involvement in occupational safety and health and with 26,000 members, it is the second largest such organisation in the world. A Chartered, 'not for profit' non-governmental organisation and registered charity, IOSH has strong links with Asia, Australia, Europe, Canada and USA. The guardian of UK generalist OSH practice standards, it provides a wide range of training courses, guidance, sector-specific specialist groups and a register of OSH consultants.

NHS Plus

NHS Plus is a network of over 100 occupational health departments in hospitals in England. They provide a variety of occupational health services to non-NHS employers with a particular focus on small and medium-sized enterprises. The NHS Plus web site (see page 81) allows businesses to identify a local NHS Plus provider and gives full contact details. In addition, the web site provides information about work-related health issues and simple guidance about how to deal with common occupational health problems.